THE STORY OF CUTLERY

Cutlery merchant's tombstone of the first century A.D. preserved at the
Vatican. The stone represents a portable sales stall exhibiting knives,
sickles and pruners that are similar to modern shapes

(By courtesy of the Sheffield City Museum)

THE STORY OF
CUTLERY

FROM FLINT TO STAINLESS STEEL

J. B. Himsworth

F.R.S.A., F.S.A.SCOT.
FREEMAN OF THE COMPANY OF CUTLERS IN HALLAMSHIRE

LONDON **ERNEST BENN** LIMITED

B53 - 15431

R2470
745.26426

Published for The Hardware Trade Journal,
by Ernest Benn Limited
Bouverie House · Fleet Street · London · EC4
Printed in Great Britain

CONTENTS

PREFACE

FOR more than seventy years I have lived close to the material of my subject, leaving school to go into my father's cutlery business when fifteen years old. Later as a craftsman and manufacturer, I carried on with my brother the family tradition of more than 220 years of active participation in the cutlery trade in the city of Sheffield. Connections by export trading were made with most parts of the world during my father's lifetime, from 1854 to 1944. For most of those ninety years, my mother also took a keen interest in the trade, especially when any question of unusual character or of an historical nature arose.

This story of cutlery through the ages was written largely as a result of my attempts to answer a number of questions that have often been put to me in one form or another. They are:

When did man first begin to use sharp tools, either found or made?

What kind of knives did he fashion for himself out of wood, stone, bronze and iron in early times—and out of steel and stainless steel when he became civilised, both as personal articles and for use in modern warfare?

What did the first knife, fork, spoon and razor look like?

When, where and by whom were the first wafer razor (safety) blades made?

Which nation produced the first pocket (shut) knife?

When did the first serrated-edge knife come into use?

When were scientific synthetic materials developed in the production of cutlery?

As the oldest member of a family that has manufactured cutlery in Sheffield for home and export markets for more than 220 years, a family whose direct ancestral settlement in Yorkshire can be traced back without a break at least 1,000 years to Saxon times, I have had extraordinary opportunities for acquiring information that have helped me to answer these questions.

Having enjoyed the privilege of acting as Master of the Sheffield

Artcrafts Guild for five years and of serving as President of the Trades Technical Preservation of Old Tools Society for another five, also as Fellow of the Royal Society of Arts, a member of the Hunter Archæological Society, Sheffield, a member of the Prehistoric Society, Cambridge, and as Freeman of the Company of Cutlers' in Hallamshire, I have taken every opportunity over the last fifty years of collecting any material which in my opinion has had a bearing on the story of cutlery.

My experience as a designer and craftsman, in addition to sixty years of manufacturing, justify, I hope, the use in my book of recollections which give it, for my part, light, shade and colour, even when they show a bias towards the 'humanities' rather than the scientific.

In my lifetime a number of far-reaching changes have occurred in the Sheffield cutlery trade which may well be termed historical.

A large number of grinding 'hulls'[1] driven by water wheels—there were approximately 400 at one period—were in use in Sheffield from about 1350. This source of power continued in decreasing measure until about 1920, overlapping steam power in factories, which was introduced in Sheffield in 1786 and had an effective run of more than 120 years. Gas engines for factory power enjoyed a short period of usefulness, the chief suppliers being a Manchester firm. Finally, electric motors ranging up to about 25 horse-power became the rule for most light trades, and for some years now self-contained motors for buffing and finishing (that is, polishing) have often been provided for each individual worker.

The compactness of modern electric motors and the readiness of the former Sheffield Electricity Supply Department (now part of the Yorkshire Electricity Board) to equip even small workshops with current for power, light and heat have been inducements for men and women, either as workers or as small manufacturers, to rent a single room for their work. The cost was small.

During the last 50 years, hand forging has been superseded in almost every branch of the trade by goffing, plating between rollers and flying out shapes by machine power. Even hardening and tempering by hand have given way largely to heat treatment in furnaces, with quenching and tempering under pyrometric control. Hand filing, too, has disappeared before the use of revolving emery and abrasive wheels. Polishing is now effected on a lathe or spindle.

Elsewhere in this *Story of Cutlery* I explain how natural materials, such as wood, horn and stag, have almost disappeared, along with pearl

[1] A room or workshop in which grinding was carried on with water, steam or electric power. There were also pig hulls (sties). Derived probably from the German word *hulle*, a mean, dirty building.

and ivory, to make way for Celluloid, plastics and other synthetic materials.

Probably the most important change has been the introduction of stainless steel. It was first offered to the cutlery trade in August 1914—the month the First World War started—as rustless, then as stainless.

A not very well-known reference from W. T. J. Jeans' *The Creators of the Age of Steel* (Chapman and Hall), although published in 1884, foreshadowed the possibility of stainless steel thirty years earlier than Harry Brearley's rediscovery and perfecting of it. On p. 294 of that book appears this statement:

> For many years it had been known that a mixture of chromium and iron could be made into a steel of great hardness and strength. Mr. Julius Baur in 1871 patented in America a way of producing chrome steel in crucibles. In 1875 Sir John Brown and Company took up the manufacture of this steel, about which little or nothing was then known in this country, and they claimed for it a remarkable degree of strength, malleability and freedom from corrosion. This steel, however, never came largely into use in this country, though some makers of edge tools had a decided preference for it.

Changes in the workers and their conditions during the last sixty years or so are no less noteworthy than the changes in the materials with which they worked. Skilled craftsmen in the 1880's felt fairly well paid with a wage of from 30s. to 35s. for a week of long hours. Purchasing power was high in some respects in those days, even if many workers had no 'Sunday clothes' or other amenities.

(The minimum wage in 1951–2 for the same kind of work is £6 per week of forty hours, rising to the £7 or £8 that is paid for first-class men, who are scarce, and while orders are plentiful—as against the fifty hours, or more, a week that was worked seventy years ago.)

The continued advances in wages, in spite of various fluctuations, combined with better housing, better food and clothing, higher educational opportunities, the wireless and greater facilities for travel, has helped to produce a highly organised class with a broader, intelligent outlook.

JOSEPH BEESTON HIMSWORTH

B. Worth & Sons & Beeston & Co.
Sheffield
1953

ACKNOWLEDGEMENTS

IN collecting material over a long period, I must express my appreciation for help, information, prompting and encouragement. First, to my parents, Beeston and Hannah Himsworth, to Edwin, my brother and partner during his lifetime, and to my sister Sabina Stokes, all of whom have since died. My wife, Dora, and daughter, Joyce, are still my dependable assistants.

W. H. Bolton, the organising secretary for a number of trade technical societies, first gave me opportunities for addressing meetings of those people interested in the practical side of the cutlery trade. These lectures offered a chance of compiling a quantity of notes on which I could develop, by research, the historical aspect of my subject. For a considerable period, my friend, C. Harry Lea, has been of untiring assistance, by voluntarily making photographic records, and in other ways.

Frank B. Colver, managing director of one of the oldest cutlery firms, has provided specimens and given information that helped to settle historical and technical points which were in doubt, while D. A. Palmer, president of the Sheffield Cutlery Manufacturers' Association, has ever been ready to talk over matters relating to the trade when it was necessary.

The late Reverend S. Keeble, author of *Industrial Day Dreams* and *The Churches' Responsibility for the Social Order*, was always strongly persuasive that I should set down in detail specialised aspects of the subject, and with Mrs. Keeble, he allowed me to dig up their lawn at Ipsden for flint tools.

Frank Turton has achieved for me what I deemed almost impossible. He collected a large number of obsolete and old trade terms once used in the Sheffield scissor trade. A unique contribution, collected from my friend and neighbour George Jowitt, describes the change from the use of natural grindstones to artificial ones. F. L. Preston has allowed me to use old family letters relating to the part that Sheffield craftsmen played in the development of the United States cutlery industry.

To Joan Smith, my niece, my thanks are due for opening up contact while in Denmark with C. L. Vebak, Curator of the Copenhagen Museum, who readily responded with some fine photographs.

My thanks are also due to J. Reale, Curator of Cirencester Museum, and to the Curator at York for allowing me to make drawings of Roman knives; also for the courtesy of Arthur Woodward and his wife of the County Museum, Los Angeles, who so speedily sent me photographs of Sheffield knives found by them in Indian graves in the United States.

Freda Neill put me in her debt by forwarding direct an aborigine stone knife and axe from Australia.

The Curator of Sheffield Museum, J. W. Baggaley, and his deputy, Arthur Walker, have often given considerable help. J. H. Whitham, the secretary of the Company of Cutlers' in Hallamshire, Allan Sykes and Mrs. Brown, of the staff, have always been available with ready and courteous attention when approached.

Thanks are also due to W. Mildon Cole, Samuel and John Marsden, Percy Shirtcliffe, the late Willis White, pearl dealer, all of whom, along with Frank M. Hughes, have supplied objects, or given help in various ways. George W. Roome, B.Sc., my elementary schoolmaster more than 65 years ago, has given me articles and still keeps a discriminating eye on his old student.

Tom Merrills, one of the few hand forgers left, has given me the benefit of his skill and experience, while H. C. Robinson made available for me his 40 years' collection of news cuttings.

I am indebted to A. L. Armstrong for specimens of flints and he, along with Dr. Arthur Court and W. H. Hanbury, has fanned the flame of interest in pre-history through the years.

I have nothing but appreciation for the way in which Alban Hills, Editor of *The Hardware Trade Journal*, has helped, as well as for the careful, understanding manner in which M. C. Hyde, the Assistant Editor, has prepared the MS. for printing.

J. B. H.

LIST OF ILLUSTRATIONS

Frontispiece. Cutler's shop of the first century, A.D.

THE PREHISTORIC

CHAPTER 1

THE PREHISTORIC

ALTHOUGH there has been some attempt in recent times, in the search for the cradle of the human race, to shift the centre of interest from Asia and northern India to Africa, the older theory is likely to be the correct one, chiefly because the most profound philosophies and religious systems appear to have originated in the East and travelled westwards. There is, in fact, a fairly well-defined track, by way of Southern Russia and the Danube, which was followed by the early inhabitants of Asia on their journey across Europe. This track is apparent whether we are considering evidence provided by human remains, tools, pottery, art or symbols.

Early tools found along this track, as well as in other parts of the world, give an account of man's physical progress as surely as a study of philosophy and religion reveals his development mentally and ethically.

The data on which our present-day knowledge of prehistoric man and the implements he used is based, have been collated from the mass of research into the early history of the world that has been carried out with such detail during the last sixty years. The story of flint cutlery could not be told now but for this research, the results of which, however, were not available to that master craftsman of France, Pagé, when he wrote his history of cutlery that was published between 1896 and 1904. Extremely well-produced in six volumes, this work contained no reference to the revolutionary discovery of stain-resisting steel, for there was no sign of its development on the industrial horizon until ten years after the last volume was published.

This nineteenth- and twentieth-century research into the prehistoric shows that the earliest tools to be shaped from hard materials, apart from a few made from bone or stag horn, do not appear to have cutting edges of any note. What are accepted as eoliths—tools of the dawn—exhibit shapes more suitable for sticking, piercing, pushing, pulling, rotating and for producing fire—hardly ever suggesting a knife or chisel edge. At an early period in history, the primitive man's teeth and nails would have been his best cutting tools, and present-day knowledge of the antiquity of man warrants the assumption that tools were first used in the early Stone Age, which gives a date of about 500,000 B.C. so far as western Europe is concerned.

When considering tools with definite cutting edges, it should be noted that the earliest no doubt attracted man's attention because of the usefulness of an edge resulting from an accidental fracture, particularly in minerals such as flint and obsidian. A volcanic glass, obsidian is exceptionally sharp and the intentional striking off of large pieces in later times justifies the belief held by some that at certain periods in the Stone Age man shaved himself.

One of the benefits of modern research into the prehistoric is that not only has it broadened our knowledge of early man, but it has also led to the co-relation of that knowledge; classification and experiment have established definite tests to differentiate between the accidental natural shaping of stone implements and artifacts that were produced by intention.

A modern illustration of the sharpness of intentionally fractured flints was given by the late T. E. Lawrence when he related[1] an incident that occurred during one of his expeditions in Arabia in the First World War. He and his men had swooped down on a railway line used by the Turks, planting explosives and noting the effects. Then, Lawrence wrote:

> We put a few miles between us and the railway before we sat down to our feast of mutton. We were short of knives, and after killing the sheep in relay, had recourse to stray flints to cut them up. As men unaccustomed to such expedients, we used them in eolithic spirit: and it came to me that if iron had been constantly rare we should have chipped our daily tools skilfully as palæoliths:[2] while we had no metal whatever, our art would have been lavished on perfect and polished stones.

A type of artifact that is especially noteworthy is the pygmy flint, which has attracted attention for two reasons. Firstly, because of its small

[1] *Seven Pillars of Wisdom* (Jonathan Cape, 1949).　　　[2] Tools of the early Stone Age.

Fig. 1. Prehistoric flints

1. Scraper from Laugerie Basse. In the Author's collection. (Compare with British Museum specimen.)
2. Scraper from Grimes Graves. (Author.)
3, 9, 11, 13 and 15. Pygmy flints from Sheffield. (A. L. Armstrong.)
4, 10, 12 and 14. Blades from Les Eyzies. (Author.)
5. Scraper from La Micoque. (Author.)
6. Scraper from Grimes Graves. (Author.)
7. Scraper with one end for piercing and the other—for scraping—with a battered back, from Upwey, Dorset. (A. L. Armstrong.)
8. Scraper from Sheffield—Blacka Moor. (Author.)
16. Tanged blade from Cresswell. (A. L. Armstrong.)

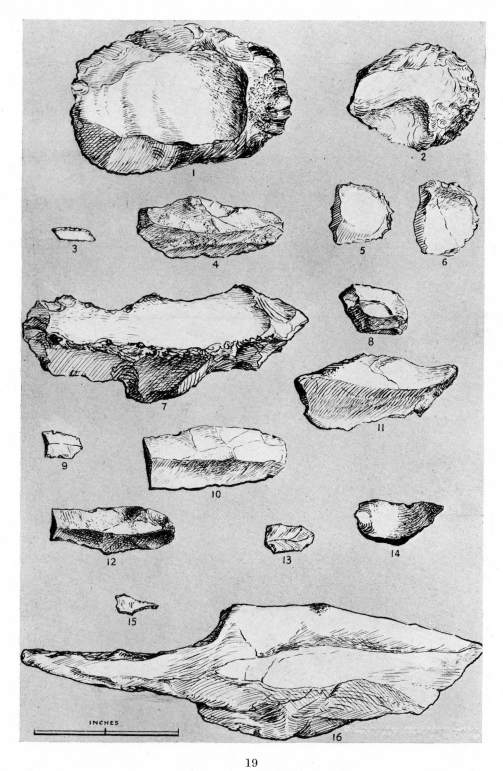

INCHES

19

size and, secondly, for its almost world-wide distribution. An assortment of fifty shaped pygmy flints found on one site at Scunthorpe, Lincolnshire, weighed less than half an ounce. This find included arrow heads measuring about $\frac{1}{4}$ in. in length, circular scrapers, crescents and other shapes. Pygmy flints were used in the older, or Palæolithic period, as well as in the later Neolithic stage and many of them exhibit remarkable precision of workmanship and a delicate sense of form. Such microliths have been found as far afield as the Crimea and Scandinavia in Europe, as well as in Africa and India. In England, they have been found in Cornwall, Wiltshire, around Hastings and in many other districts (Fig. 1).

The Sheffield area is well represented in the Gatty collection and by the efforts of A. Leslie Armstrong and W. M. Cole, who have found specimens on Broomhead, Burbage, Derwent and other local moors. In the Huddersfield and Blackstone Edge district many pygmy flints have been found, chiefly near altitudes of 1,000 ft.

It has been suggested that in some districts these artifacts were originally used for reinforcing harpoons for fishing and, as tools mounted in handles, for a number of other purposes, including pointing arrows and darts. Circular-shaped sickles embodying this type of flint as teeth have come down through the ages, as also has a tool, which with similar teeth set in a straight line, was probably used for sawing.

From Palæolithic times have come scrapers and blades of different shapes and sizes, but it was not until the age of Neolithic tools that any-

---

Fig. 2. Flint, iron and bronze implements

(*Top*). These prehistoric flint tools were discovered in a small section of two earthwork rings at Berin's Hill, Ipsden, Oxford, on the property of the Reverend and Mrs. S. E. Keeble, by the Author and Joyce R. Himsworth

1. A ficron. (Compare with *Prehistoric Society Proceedings*, January–July, 1939–11.)
2. Point for tattooing (?). (Compare with that found by Lilia and Homer H. Kidder in a Magdalenian rock shelter at Pay-de-Lacun (Corrèze), Southern France.)
3. Hollow scraper for wooden shafts. (Compare with specimens in British Museum.)
4. Arrow head, yellow and water rolled.
5. Knife with battered back.
6. Borer. (Compare with specimens in British Museum.)
7. Scraper with hinged fracture.
8. Scraper, carefully fashioned.

(*Bottom*). These implements were all found in Yorkshire

1, 5, 6 and 7. Flint knives, chiefly from Settle, Malham Cove and the Craven districts of Yorkshire.
2. Iron knife blade from Skipton. Early Medieval.
3. Iron knife blade and stag horn handle, from Skipton.
4. Bronze razor. (In the Skipton Museum collection.)

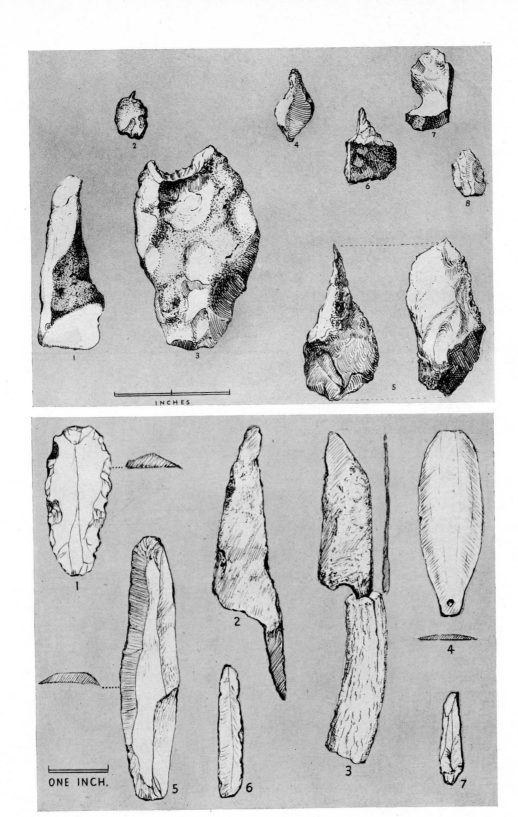

INCHES

ONE INCH.

21

thing approaching the present-day conception of a knife was fashioned. Then appeared the more or less wedge-shaped axe, which was beautifully formed, as were the knives, made with tangs to take handles of wood or stag horn, daggers, spears, arrow-heads and sickles that came from the same period. Some specimens of Neolithic knives are still so sharp that they will roughly point a lead pencil.

Early flint tools often show signs of having been reshaped or sharpened in later periods. The arrangement of convex and concave surfaces, of bevels and flats in most of these tools present a satisfying appearance even to the eye of a critical modern craftsman.

Cutting tools of the early Stone Age have been found in greater numbers in the south of Britain than in the Sheffield area. The Ice Age lasted longer in the north and prehistoric man did not find the conditions there very encouraging, particularly for food supplies. Even in Neolithic and Bronze Age times, it appears that the cold gritstone crags, clay beds and forests surrounding Sheffield were visited only occasionally, while settlements for hunting during the summer were of a temporary nature.

Winter quarters were in the softer, milder conditions of the north-east of Nottinghamshire and the Trent Valley of Lincolnshire. Glacial drifts and gravels there as well as in south Derbyshire and Staffordshire contain sites that have yielded fairly prolific numbers of tools representative of Palæolithic times.

The Neolithic or New Stone Age (from 8000 to 2300 B.C.) has also produced large quantities of flints. Stone sickles and knives from this period that have been found in Yorkshire and western Europe were developed in style from flints used earlier in southern France and ancient Egypt. This process of development would have been spread over a long period, with different styles in the fashioning of stone passing gradually from one district to another.

There were centres of production even in the Stone Age and one well known centre, Grimes Graves in Norfolk, has been termed the 'Sheffield of the Stone Age' on account of the large quantity of materials and finished tools found there (Fig. 1).

A small centre where an unusual type of slate knife was made in the Stone Age was discovered about 50 years ago, when nearly 150 interments in stone cists were unearthed in the prehistoric cemetery at Harlyn Bay, Cornwall. It seems that a peace-loving trading community lived there, as few weapons were found among the many slate objects in the graves.

The knives discovered at Harlyn Bay bear a remarkable similarity to the table knives of to-day, both in size and shape. The design suggests an elemental pattern that was intended mainly for the purpose of eating, rather than for attack. From remains found on the site, the knives appear to have been used for eating shell-fish.

Flint is usually looked upon as the most important cutting material of the Stone Age—comparatively little is recorded of the use of other materials, which gives the Harlyn Bay slate knives an unusual interest.

Fig. 3. Slate knife (*circa* 500 B.C.), from Harlyn Bay, Cornwall. Measuring 11 in., this knife is very similar to the present-day table knife

Flint tools were not only in use in Palæolithic and Neolithic times, but they were also to be found well into the Bronze Age, particularly in districts where hard materials or metals were scarce. Both stone and bronze tools are sometimes found to have been buried together in interments. The transition from the use of one material to the other would have taken a slow but natural course in some parts of the world. Other districts, perhaps as the result of invasion, might have changed over more quickly, even quicker than changes in styles of architecture, or as rapidly as Sheffield turned from carbon to stainless steel knives.

In some countries, the transition from the Stone Age has yet to be made—the stone tools that are fashioned by the present-day bush aborigines of Western Australia are, for instance, almost identical to those of pre-historic man. How the aborigines make their flint tools is described in *Stone-Age Bushmen To-day* (Blackie, 1936), by J. R. B. Love, who says:

> While the women are away hunting, the main occupation of the men is making stone spearheads . . . with finely serrated edges, they are made by percussion, then flaking by pressure with stone, bone and wood tools, from several kinds of fissile stone. The native will take up a piece of broken rock, the size of his fist . . . test it by striking it with any convenient lump of stone lying about that will serve as a hammer. . . . If it flakes nicely he will break it down to somewhere near the size of a spearhead and put it in his wallet, to be dressed into shape at leisure in his camp. . . . Inside his bark wallet is a snug nest of down, usually of bullrush, in which rest spearheads, pieces of stone in different stages of manufacture, the tools used in their making, and nowadays . . . perhaps a small bit of tobacco.
>
> In making a stone spearhead he uses a slab of sandstone for an anvil on which he places a 'cushion' consisting of several layers of paper bark. With a blunt

pointed stick of hardwood, a foot long, he presses on the edge of the small stone, placed on the anvil, and breaks off a flake. Turning the stone, he continues until he has roughed out the spearhead. He next takes a piece of kangaroo's thigh bone, ground to a point on a rough stone and presses flakes away from the edges of the spearhead till it has reached the finished shape. The final stage is now to take a thin bone ground to a fine edge, and serrate the edges of the spearhead by pressing out the tiny flakes from the sharp edges. The whole work of making these spearheads is a highly skilled art. Some of the stones are semi-precious, as agates and crystals. . . . When the stone is finally shaped, serrated and complete, the artist (for artist is the proper name for him) puts his new spearhead in his mouth, wets it and holds it up to appraise its beauty and keen point. If it is a translucent stone, he holds it up to the light and lovingly ponders over its colour.

Pygmy stone implements are found in many parts of Australia.

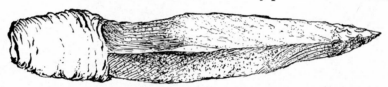

Fig. 4. Australian stone knife for making ceremonial incisions. Total length is 7½ in. From Groote Eylandt, Gulf of Carpentaria, per Mr. H. L. Perriman, missionary from 1921–36

Another primitive tool that has come down through the ages and is still in use to-day is the bamboo knife, described by Dr. A. C. Haddon in his *Head Hunters* (Methuen, 1902), which recorded his visit to British New Guinea in 1882. Dr. Haddon, who obtained two of these knives, gives a detailed account of their manufacture and uses:

After a man is killed (in the islands of Kiwai and Mawata) his head is cut off with a bamboo knife; the blade is made of a split piece of bamboo, the handle

---

Fig. 5. Flint implements and knives from Derbyshire, Yorkshire, Scotland, Scandinavia and Australia

1. ¾-in. scraper, or currier's knife.
2. 1¾-in. scraper, or currier's knife.
3. Sickle and teeth.
4. 4½-in. flint from Derbyshire.
5. 7-in. flint dagger from Belgium.
6 and 7. Slug knives from Scotland.
8. 7½-in. Scandinavian dagger.
9. Flint knife from Yorkshire.
10. Australian flint knife.
11 and 12. Obsidian daggers from Yucatan.
13 and 14. Flint knives from Derbyshire.

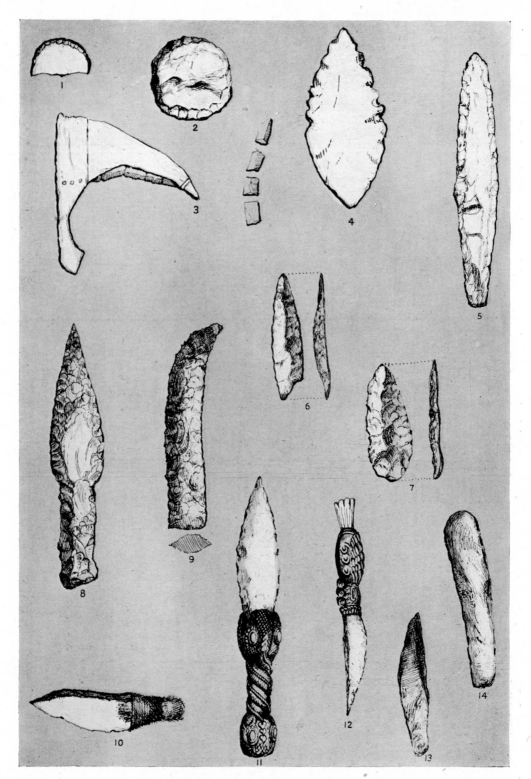

being bound round with plaited string. When the knife is to be used, a nick is made on the edge, close to the handle, with a small shell; then a strip is peeled off from the other end, the nick preventing the handle from splitting. The rind of bamboo is full of minute flinty particles, so much so that a fresh cut edge is very sharp, and will cut off a man's head; but it will oblige only for one such occasion, and a fresh edge has to be made for each head that is cut off. One knife I bought had five nicks, which means it had been used for the purpose of cutting off the heads of five people, and another had nine notches.

Dr. Haddon saw the natives tattooing themselves, using burnt resin as a pigment and puncturing the skin with a thorn, which was tapped lightly with a stick.

Users of primitive tools, however, cannot all be dismissed as barbarians incapable of appreciating the merit of quality in workmanship. Although the prehistoric beings who fashioned them may have been of a low order mentally, Scandinavian tools and blades, for instance, reveal a high standard of craftsmanship. The flaking is regular and the shapes exhibit well-planned edges and contours. Ripple-flaked arrow heads found in the West Riding of Yorkshire possibly reflect the influence of this workmanship.

With the probable exception of Egypt, nowhere was the art of flaking and retouching brought to such perfection as in Denmark at the end of the Stone Age. The remarkable quality of Danish flints can be judged from the specimens shown in Figs. 5 and 6. Egyptian gold-mounted ceremonial flint knives and South American obsidian knives with mosaic handles, although devised for barbaric sacrificial customs, were often works of great artistic merit, skilfully fashioned by craftsmen.

Another example of the high standard of quality often to be found in prehistoric flint tools is a dagger that was discovered in May 1935, some 7 ft. below the surface of a bog in northern Hanover by two labourers who were cutting peat. In its *Journal* of January-June 1937, the Prehistoric Society described it as being a 'flint dagger complete with wooden handle and leather sheath with belt'.

The handle of the dagger was bound with a fabric of sheep, goat, cow and horse hair, encased in a hollowed-out piece of wood, probably alder. The sheath was of sheep leather and consisted of two parts: a narrow guard, or reinforcement, for the edge of the blade; and the sheath proper, which on one face was sewn together at the tip, while the other carried a lightly incised decoration of a herring-bone pattern. Of all the hundreds of daggers of this type that have been discovered, this is the only one to have been unearthed with its sheath and fittings.

Skill in fashioning stone or mineral implements was not confined to

Fig. 6. Scandinavian flint daggers

The first dagger measures 13 in. long. The broad specimen (third from left) is thin in the blade with a much thicker handle and demonstrates the degree of symmetry achieved by early craftsmen. This dagger came from the island of Fyn, but originated in Jutland, from whence similar implements found their way to other countries in late Stone and Bronze Age times. The second dagger served as a spear head and was found, in a simple form, in early Dolmens. The five Danish flint daggers on the right are of early and middle periods. It is thought that in the Neolithic period it must have been customary to carry this style of dagger in the belt. The fourth from the left measures about 11 in. long.

certain countries or districts, for the early inhabitants of East Africa, for example, made their tools to a standard that was comparable to many of the flints of western Europe, although it is doubtful if they were as artistically produced as the ornamental daggers of Egypt.

The use of obsidian blades in Kenya during the Aurignacian period has been described in detail by L. S. B. Leakey, an authority on Kenya. In his *The Stone Age Cultures of Kenya Colony* (Cambridge University Press, 1931) Mr. Leakey said that these—

> points with their sharp cutting edge and blunted backs closely resemble pen knife blades, although some of them are very small. On May 6 1929, I made an experiment of skinning and disembowelling a Thomson's gazelle, which is about the size of a goat, with a single backed 'blade' about $1\frac{1}{2}$ in. long. I finished the job easily in 20 minutes unaided and the backed blade used was still quite sharp at the end of the process.

Mr. Leakey said that this backed blade had been buried in a cave deposit for something over 25,000 years. Also describing these obsidian blades, he wrote:

> The essential characters of the ordinary knives which we use to-day for cutting meat, for skinning animals, and for sharpening pieces of wood, are really a sharp cutting edge and a blunt back. The object of the blunt back is that we may lay a finger along it, and by that means not only exert pressure, but also control the movements of the blade. If we take our Aurignacian blade of the type known as a backed blade, we find it embodies both these characters, and that even in its shape it is similar to many a steel knife blade of to-day.

Some of the comparatively modern obsidian knives of the South Sea Islands, which are slightly larger than these Kenyan Aurignacian tools, are fitted with handles made by the application of bark and resin. Unlike the Aurignacian knives, they are often double-edged, being shaped without a blunt back. It is notable that obsidian blades were used for shaving in pre-Mycenean times, the mode of fracture being such as to make the edge of the flake particularly effective as a razor.

For some time after flint and obsidian were being used to fashion cutting tools, prehistoric man would have continued to use his hands for tearing up food and transferring it to his mouth. An interesting but more modern account of what can be accomplished without the aid of cutlery was given by T. E. Lawrence in *Seven Pillars of Wisdom* (Cape, 1949):

> . . . two men came staggering through the thrilled crowd, carrying the rice and meat on a tinned copper tray or shallow dish, five feet across . . . In the tribe, there was only this one food bowl of the size, and an incised inscription ran round it in florid Arabic characters: 'To the glory of God, and in trust of

mercy at the last, the property of His poor suppliant, Auda abu Tayi'. . . .
The bowl was now brim-full, ringed round its edge with an embankment of
white rice a foot wide and six inches deep, filled with legs and ribs of mutton
till they toppled over.

Manners demanded that the guests should feign indifference, but by
slow stages their attention was drawn to the necessity of eating as the host
Nasir approached the dish. The twenty-two guests grouped themselves
round it on one knee:

> We turned back our tight sleeves to the elbow, and taking lead from Nasir
> with a low 'In the name of God the merciful, the loving kind', we dipped
> together. . . . We would knead between the fingers (not soiling the palm)
> neat balls of rice and fat and liver and meat cemented by gentle pressure,
> and project them by leverage of the thumb, from the crooked fore-finger
> into the mouth. . . .
>
> As the meat pile wore down (nobody really cared about rice: flesh was the
> luxury) one of the chief Howeitat eating with us would draw his dagger, silver
> hilted, set with turquoise, a signed masterpiece of Mohammed ibn Zari, of
> Yauf, and would cut criss-cross from the larger bones long diamonds of meat
> easily torn up between the fingers, for it was necessarily boiled very tender,
> since all had to be disposed of with the right hand which alone was honour-
> able. At top speed we twisted, tore, cut and stuffed; never speaking, since
> conversation would insult a meal's quality, though it was proper to smile thanks
> when an intimate guest passed a select fragment, or when Mohammed al
> Dheilan gravely handed over a large barren bone with a blessing.

BRONZE, IRON AND
MEDIEVAL PERIODS

CHAPTER 2

BRONZE, IRON AND MEDIEVAL PERIODS

THE oldest code of law in the world—that of Hammurabi, who lived about 2100 B.C.—shows that metal knives were in use at that time, at any rate for surgical purposes. One section of the Babylonian inscription that was discovered at Susa decreed that:

> If a doctor has treated a man with a metal knife for a severe wound and has cured him, or has opened a man's tumour with a metal knife, then he shall receive ten shekels of silver.

If the patient died or his eye was destroyed, then it was laid down that the doctor would be punished by the cutting-off of his hands.

It is not possible to say whether this ancient law referred to iron or bronze knives, but of the two metals bronze is the more likely.

It may be assumed that in some parts of the world, the Bronze Age originated in approximately 2000 B.C., or about the time that metal surgical knives were being used in Babylon. Copper, which is the main constituent of bronze, was being worked from mines that were already well established in Egypt by 1000 B.C., and it appears that many of the ancient Egyptian carvings were effected with non-ferrous tools.

The Bronze Age reached Britain about 1300 B.C., having an effective influence of only some 1,000 years—that is, until 300 B.C.—although it overlapped to a certain extent into the age of iron. That the Bronze Age was late in reaching Britain was possibly due to the distance separating that country from the centres of world cultures, which have been recognised as being Uralian, Danubian and Mediterranean. It should also be borne in mind that the glacial conditions that retarded the settlement of the north of England (to which reference has been made in Chapter I) would have also delayed the development of the use of bronze.

Many historians have assumed that in conquering Britain, the legions of the Roman Emperor Cæsar used iron weapons, while those of the defending Britons were of bronze. This suggests that bronze was still being worked in this country at a time when iron was in vogue in other countries, a theory that may hold good for much of Britain, but which cannot be accepted as true for the whole of the country, for iron tools have been discovered at the Glastonbury Lake Dwellings, which are believed to have been sacked before the Roman invasion.

Although bronze objects have not been discovered in any great numbers in cinerary urns of the Bronze Age, bronze razors have been found on sites over a wide area of western and central Europe and, to a lesser extent, in Britain. The type most frequently met had a thin, flat blade and was at times given a decorative finish, but, although the metal was usually thickened at the centre, it was made without a midrib. It has been suggested that some types of bronze razors reached Britain from the Mediterranean area (Fig. 2, No. 4, Bottom).

In late Bronze Age times, the blade was 'bifid' at the centre—that is, split. Both the single and bifid types were made by casting and then hammered into shape. A number of specimens that are now housed in the Weston Park Museum, Sheffield, measure 4 in. in length.

The Bronze Age lasted longer in some countries than in others, and it seems certain that in a number of districts bronze razors were still being used after iron had been introduced for other purposes.

The most complete account of bronze razors found in the British Isles is probably that given by Mrs. C. M. Piggott in the *Proceedings of the Prehistoric Society* (of Cambridge) of 1946, in which she described four types—namely, plain, decorated, bifid and those showing foreign influence, classified as 'exotic'.

Evidence given to support the belief that Bronze Age man used razors for shaving, apart from their probable ceremonial use before burial, is based on the appearance of prehistoric human remains. The arrangement of bronze razors and associated objects into a chronological order, with other considerations, led Mrs. Piggott to suggest that razors were made at a date earlier than the eighth century in the British Isles. She said that the earliest type appeared to have been developed from even earlier bronze and, probably, flint knives, and was used by a people of a 'food-vessel culture' who had a long acquaintance with the manufacture of oval flint knives. Provenance is given of ninety-seven specimens of bronze razors, some having straight tangs designed to take knocked-on handles, others being pierced with a hole in a flat tang for pinning into scales, probably after the fashion of the modern shut razor.

Bronze daggers, which are sometimes found to have been interred together with razors in Bronze Age graves, played an important part in the life of the Bronze Age man, for, as in most other metal periods, they were an all-purpose tool. Used for attack, for defence and for cutting up food, they would have been kept readily available and much treasured by their owners. Bronze daggers, like razors, were usually cast in stone moulds and then subjected to much hammering to thin and toughen them. Those with tangs had handles knocked on, but the type that was in most general use had flat double-edged blades with flat tangs and riveted handles.

That bronze tools can possess good cutting qualities often occasions surprise, but as recently as the 1939–45 World War bronze scissors were in demand for use in munition factories, because of the danger of sparking from ferrous tools. This is an example of a modern application for scissors, but the earliest types of iron scissors, specimens of which have been discovered in both France and Germany, dating from about 250 to 150 B.C., were shaped like present-day hand sheep shears.

The Use of Iron

There is much evidence to support the argument that to follow the Aryan race in its travels from Asia across Europe will show how the use of iron originally spread. Cuneiform inscribed clay documents refer to the working of iron in very early times in Asia Minor.

In Mycenean times, it appears that iron was used for ornamentation only, which suggests that it was then a scarce and precious metal. Flinders Petrie states that iron was little known in Egypt until about 800 B.C.; a knife that has been credited to this period was made of thin iron with a bronze handle. Petrie believes, however, that at an earlier date iron tools with a cutting edge of steel-like quality were produced by case hardening in Assyria.

The fact that of the 50,000 objects of all descriptions that were found in Tutankhamen's tomb and which are now housed in Cairo Museum, only twelve or thirteen were of iron, is recorded in Volume 3 of Howard Carter's account of the discovery of the tomb.[1] He says that the Egyptians did not use iron, except on rare occasions. A conservative people, they were metallurgists of copper and bronze and all their wonderful work was performed with these metals.

An iron dagger that was found on the mummy of Tutankhamen establishes, however, that iron was being worked in about the year 1000 B.C. On the dagger, which was encased in a gold sheath covered with floral and zoomorphic motifs, was a haft of gold with a knob of cloisonné enamel and gold wire. After lying some 3,000 years in the tomb before its discovery by Howard Carter, the iron blade was still bright, with only a few spots of rust.

[1] *The Tomb of Tut-Ankhamen* by Howard Carter and A. Mace (Cassell, 3 vols., 1922–33).

It is probable that meteoric iron was used for fashioning tools at an early date, and the fact that there was a percentage of nickel in its composition might account for the comparative rustlessness of some articles that have been found thousands of years after they were made. Damp-resisting materials that were used in preparing a mummy would also have afforded a certain amount of protection.

Howard Carter regarded this discovery as astounding, for the owner of the dagger lived in the Age of Bronze; he concludes, therefore, that iron was at that time a precious metal to the Egyptians, confirming the belief of Flinders Petrie, mentioned earlier in this chapter.

Among the other implements discovered in Tutankhamen's tomb was a gold dagger which, shaped with two grooves down the centre, had a well-hardened blade, effected probably by hammering. A remarkable specimen of craftsmanship and design, the handle was ornamented with cloisonné and bands of gold wire in looped and twisted designs, as well as fine, granulated beads of the same metal.

As recently as 1911, American archæologists claimed to have discovered an iron spear head in XII Dynasty deposits in Egypt, an assumption that, if correct, suggests a date of about 2000 B.C.

Iron objects appear to have been used in Britain as early as 300 B.C. and were possibly brought into the country by invading forces. The Romans are credited by some historians as having introduced iron tools and weapons to the Britons, but the Lake Dwellings of Glastonbury—of an earlier date—have provided thirteen iron knives as evidence that iron was worked in Britain before the Romans arrived.

These knives were of different types and sizes. One of the larger specimens was shaped like a chopper and had been made with a tang. Another of the knives was double-edged, while a third, which had a long, narrow blade with a longitudinal groove near the back edge on both sides,

---

Fig. 7. Iron razors and implements

(*Top*). Danish razors and scissors of the Iron Age (two-thirds scale)

In the late Iron Age (300 B.C.) warriors were interred with their razors (1, 2 and 3) as well as their swords. Diodorus of Sicily spoke of Gauls with shaven cheeks and long drooping moustaches. The scissors (4) are of the shear or flexible type and in the smaller sizes were made of bronze, while iron was used for the larger types.

(*Bottom*). Iron implements of Roman and African origin

Top left is a Roman knife, while left to right are two Roman butchers' knives; pruner; cook's knife; dagger; African sacrificial knife; and an execution knife from Central Africa.

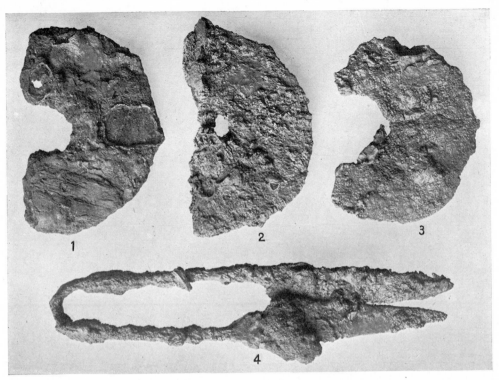

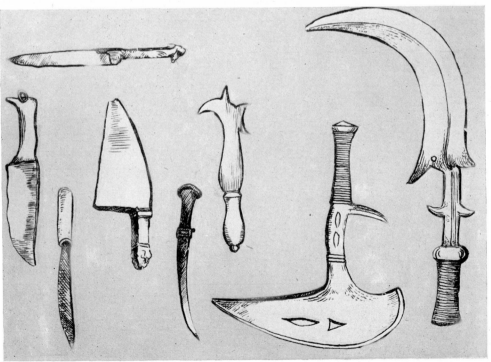

appears to have been produced by forging, in a similar way to the *scramasax* that the Saxons made a few hundred years later.

Many more iron tools were found at the same time, together with several handles, eight of which had been fashioned from roe-deer antlers and thirty-three others from antlers of red deer. Some of the handles were slit lengthwise to take a blade tang, while others had been perforated in the broad end of the tine to take a pin. Five of the handles were found to have been fastened to the iron tangs by one, or sometimes two, rivets.

Professor Boyd Dawkins considers that Glastonbury was probably sacked shortly before the Roman Conquest. From this and other evidence it may be assumed that not only were iron tools used in Britain before the Roman invasion, but also that hafted knives with a slit or slotted handle have been known in Britain for nearly 2,000 years. The modern farriers' knife with its slotted reindeer handle is a surviving example of these ancient Glastonbury tools.

As an instance of the overlapping of the Bronze Age into the Age of Iron, it is noteworthy that in this Lake Village at Glastonbury, with its 269 dwelling hearths, archæologists have discovered 274 objects made of bronze as well as 111 articles of iron. While none of the bronze implements had sharp edges for cutting, nearly half of the iron tools were made to cut. In this pre-Roman conquest village, bow sticks for boring were also found, together with bill-hooks, gouges, adzes, files, saws, and a furnace with crucibles and slag.

Scissors of the shear or flexible type, found to have been interred along with iron swords and razors in the graves of warriors, were also made in the two metals—bronze being used for smaller sizes and iron for the larger types. An iron knife blade discovered at Borran's Camp, near Grassington in Yorkshire, which is now housed in Skipton Museum, is believed to be of Roman origin, for the district was peopled by the Brigantes in their last stand against the Romans.

Relics of the Iron Age, said to date from the second century A.D., have also been found in Scotland. They include furnaces, crucibles, crucible

---

Fig. 8. Bronze and iron daggers and knives
(*Top*). 1. Cypriote type bronze knife. 2, 3, 4. Early bronze daggers.
(*Bottom*). Iron Age implements—specimens 1, 2, 3, 4, and 6 coming from the Glastonbury Lake Dwellings.

1. Knife handle.
2. 5¾-in. knife.
3. 4-in. knife.
4. 9-in. dagger.
5. 12-in. Saxon scramasax.
6. 10½-in. sickle.

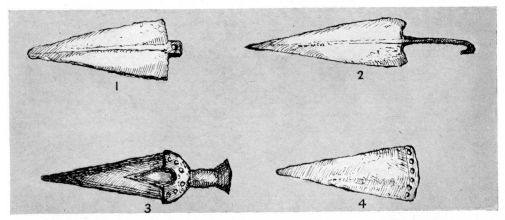

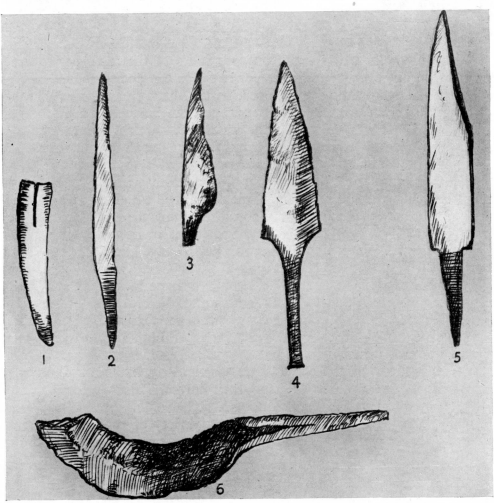

tongs, spongy iron and slag, and, as some of them were discovered as far north as the isles of Skye, Orkney and Shetland, it has been assumed that fuel must have been shipped there from the mainland.

The great deposits of slag that are to be found in the Forest of Dean and in parts of Sussex were made during the Roman occupation.

Fig. 9. Iron shears from the Glastonbury Lake Dwellings, which have their modern counterpart in patterns of hand sheep shears

Perhaps the most important cutlery relics of the same period are a number of pocket, or shut, knives, for as far as can be ascertained Roman pocket knives were the first to appear in the history of the world. Made without the spring or the nail nick to open the blade that are found on modern pocket knives, they had bone scales that were checkered or banded across with lines. On one of these Roman knives, now in the British Museum, is to be found the maker's name.

Roman knives made for general use were mostly scimitar-shaped, some of them having round, thin tangs, while others had scale tangs on to which were pinned bone scales; a ring or loop for hanging the knife from the belt forming part of the end of the tang. Specimens of iron knives that were made for the use of surgeons during this period have also been found.

A typical stone tank on Hadrian's Wall at Corstopitum (Corbridge), Northumberland, that was worn to a concave shape by Roman soldiers by sharpening their knives and swords is illustrated in Fig. 13. The stone is a fine-grained sandstone of a similar composition and texture to much of those in the Sheffield neighbourhood, which for several hundreds of years were quarried to provide grindstones before synthetic stones were introduced in the nineteenth century. Some people, particularly butchers, to-day still prefer this natural stone for whetting their knives. This Roman stone tank was photographed by the Author in 1952.

The Romans made their cutlery in a variety of patterns and sizes. Butchers' knives were produced in sizes ranging from 6 in. to 9 in. in total length, while Roman scissors or shears varied from 5 in. overall to 12 in. Pocket knives when shut measured about 3 in. in length.

How the Roman cutler made his products and how they were disposed of to his fellow citizens is recorded on the tombstones of two cutlers of the first century A.D. that have been preserved in the Vatican. On one of them two men are depicted forging on an anvil with a fire in the background. Above them, on what possibly represents the chimney breast of the hearth, are suspended a number of tools, such as tongs, a knife that closely resembles a butcher's cleaver, and a sickle.

On the other tombstone—which is reproduced as the frontispiece of this book—is depicted a cutlery sales-shop, or market stall, in which two

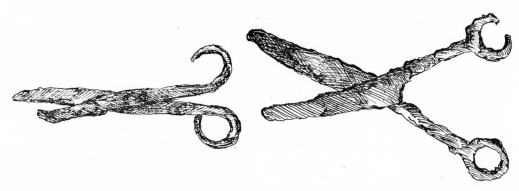

Figs. 10. and 11. Early Roman iron scissors. These Roman patterns are among the world's earliest scissors

men are shown with their wares. Nine of these knives are similar to present-day styles of butchers' or hunting knives, while twelve other tools include sickles, pruning knives and what may be bill-hooks.

Saxon and Medieval Cutlery

In Saxon England, a period which lasted from the fifth century to the eleventh century, the knife next in importance to the sword was the *scramasax*, which never left its owner, day or night. Through all man's upward struggles from the prehistoric to the nineteenth century, a knife at the belt for either defence or attack came next to his five senses. Generally, the Scandinavian or Viking *scramasax* approximated more to the size of a sword, while the Saxon weapon was more in the nature of a dagger.

Occasionally, the Saxon *scramasax* was damascened or inlaid with an inscription, which might include the name of the owner. This custom of putting a maker's name or mark on a knife started quite early in Roman times, and inscribed knives lead right up to Sheffield twentieth-century products. Not only were the early marks an indication of geographical origin, but also often suggested the purpose for which the knife was intended. Sometimes the graces to be sung at meat would be included, while mottoes and proverbs, with appropriate music, were also inscribed in this way. The 'grace-before-meat' variety was usually inscribed on a large carving or serving blade, as the space that could be filled was correspondingly large.

Inlaid on the blade of a Saxon *scramasax* to be seen in the British Museum are the words 'Gebereht owns me', while on another the Runic alphabet has been inscribed in brass and silver; one of these specimens of the *scramasax* is illustrated in Fig. 12. The Victoria and Albert Museum, London, possesses a blade of later date that is inscribed with the music of the first tenor's part of two graces.

Fig. 12. A Saxon scramasax pattern damascened, the inscription reads "Gebereht owns me"
(*Circa* A.D. 900–1000. British Museum, *Anglo Saxon Guide*, 1923, p. 95.)

Table forks were not generally known or required in Saxon or medieval times. The knives in most general use in those periods were narrow and of graceful proportions, with a sharp point that could be used as a prong to pick up food after it had been cut. This form of blade, which was developed from that general utility tool, the *scramasax*, or dagger, was carried at the belt. The housewife of the Middle Ages and later times also carried her knives suspended by a cord or chain from the girdle.

The dagger lost much of its importance when Europe became more civilised and its peoples adopted more settled habits, for men then began to fight their battles with mechanised implements of warfare, as opposed to hand-to-hand fighting. Apart from its popularity as a hunting knife and its continued use by butchers, the dagger afterwards became mainly an article of dress.

Fig. 13. Early forks and spoon; spoon moulds; and a stone tank

1, 2. Reverse and front of the earliest hall-marked fork (1632) showing the arms of John Manners of Haddon Hall. The size is $6\frac{7}{8}$-in.

3. Moulds in which Britannia metal spoons were cast in the eighteenth and nineteenth centuries. (*By courtesy of Hull Museum.*)

4. Anglo-Saxon silver spoon and fork discovered at Skevington, Wiltshire. They measure 8 in. long and probably date from the ninth century. This eating fork is believed to be the earliest found in England. (British Museum, *Anglo Saxon Guide*, 1923, p. 107.)

5. A typical stone tank on Hadrian's Wall at Corstopitum (Corbridge), Northumberland, that was worn to this shape by Roman soldiers sharpening their knives and swords.

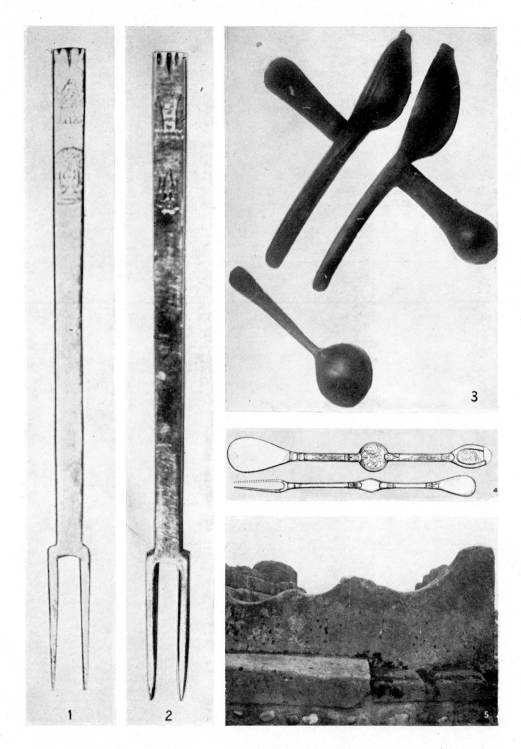

1

2

3

4

5

43

A natural development of the dagger was its use as a table knife, with the point turned upward and rounded. This meant that the blade could no longer be utilised to pick up food and transfer it to the mouth, a factor that led to the introduction of the fork to help keep the fingers clean.

The fork must have been a most welcome addition to early table cutlery, for according to a fifteenth-century writer on table manners it was not correct to grab food with both hands, but rather meat should be taken with three fingers only and not too much should be put into the mouth at once. It was not good manners to scratch oneself at meals and then put the fingers in the food, while greasy fingers should not be licked or rubbed on a jacket, but should be wiped clean on a napkin!

The earliest known reference to a fork being used at an English table was made in 1611, when it appears that this implement was introduced into the country by an Englishman on his return from travel in Italy and Germany. A silver fork in the Victoria and Albert Museum, with a London hallmark of 1632, has two prongs and is possibly the earliest hall-marked silver fork to be made in Britain (Fig. 13).

Although there are no traces of forks having been used to any extent during Saxon or medieval times, it is curious that an Anglo-Saxon silver fork and spoon have been found at Skevington, Wiltshire (Fig. 13). Measuring 8 in. in length and dating from the ninth century, it is probably the earliest eating fork to have been discovered in England.

SHEFFIELD AND
ITS CUTLERY HISTORY

POUR Y PARVENIR A BONNE FOI

CHAPTER 3

SHEFFIELD AND ITS CUTLERY HISTORY

SHEFFIELD came into focus as a centre of note at the time of the Norman Conquest of England and the erection shortly afterwards of a castle on a site that was previously occupied in Roman, Saxon and medieval times. Some relics of these periods, together with slight evidence of prehistoric occupation, came to light during excavations in 1927.

Professor John Ruskin, when asked why he had placed his museum in Sheffield, replied:

> 'In Cutlers' ironwork we have (in the town of Sheffield) at this epoch of our history, the best of its kind, done by English hands, unsurpassable, I presume, when the workman chooses to do all he knows, by that of any living nation.'

Sheffield cutlery, so far as documentary evidence is concerned, was first referred to in the Yorkshire Lay Subsidies of the reign of Edward I (1272–1307), from which the following extracts, recorded in the Yorkshire Archæological Society's Record Series, are taken:

Schefeld	
Nonus deu ville de Schefeld	A.D. 1297
Robertus le Coteler: j vaccam, xs; iiij quart. avene, iiijs. Summa ixs.	xijd.
Stephanus Cissor: j vaccum, vs; vij oves, iijs vjd; v quart. avene, vs. Summa xiijs vjd.	xviijd.
Jurdanus Cissor; j vaccam, vs, iiij quart. avene, iiijs. Summa ixs.	xijd.
Simon Cissor; j vaccam, j boviculum, xvd; v. quart. avene. vs; Summa xjs iijd.	xvd.

Periodically, Sheffield in the West Riding of Yorkshire is called on to re-establish its claims to antiquity, its early manufacture of cutlery and its reputation for high-quality wares. Several times during the last sixty years, Sheffield, Sussex, has been said to be the probable provenance of the 'Schefeld Thwytel' that Chaucer mentioned in the fourteenth century in his tales of the Pilgrimage to Canterbury, because, it was argued, the route lay nearer to Sussex than Yorkshire.

There is, however, no evidence that Sheffield in Sussex existed as a village before 1577, in which year an iron forge—that was to last for only some seventy years—was established.

Sheffield, Yorkshire, on the other hand, is recorded in the Doomsday survey as 'Escafeld', and a substantial castle arose there between 1250 and 1270 on the site of an earlier one. A church was constructed about the year 1110, and a market held in Sheffield was of such importance in 1297 that the Lord of the Manor granted certain rights by charter in connection with it.

An 'inquisition' of 1332 established that forges (*forgia*) were being used in Sheffield at that time and the evidence of the reference to 'one cuttellum de Shefeld' in the wardrobe of Edward III (1327–77) certainly cannot be ignored.

It is also recorded that Chaucer (1340–1400) lived for a time at Hatfield, near Doncaster, only eighteen miles from Sheffield. So when we read:

> A Schefeld thwytel bare he in his hose
> Ronde was his face and camois was his nose

it may safely be assumed that Chaucer alluded to a knife that was produced on the banks of the River Don, Yorkshire.

It is worth recalling an old piece of doggerel that runs:

> In the brave days of old when Sheffield Castle stood, and all the country round about was hill and moor and wood; there was no Master Cutler then, but there were cutlers by the score, who worked on the banks of the River Don, as their sires had done before.

During the excavations which were carried out on the site of Sheffield Castle during the years 1927 to 1929, knives that are typical of the whittle of Chaucer's time were found at a fourteenth-fifteenth-century level. Probably, the descendant of the Saxon *scramasax*, the whittle was also an all-purpose knife, used for eating, for working and for defence. It was carried in a sheath at the girdle and had a pointed tang in the handle—a style that is still produced in Sheffield and which is to-day known as a 'whittle-tang' (Fig. 14).

Another early knife that has a modern counterpart is the capped Sheffield knife, which a certain Robert Laneham mentioned in a letter that he wrote in 1575. Such knives were made with either a box-like cap at the end of the handle, or a piece of flat metal; both of these styles being in present-day use, particularly when the blades are mounted with stag-horn handles (Fig. 27).

In more recent times, Sheffield has been most favourably placed for the production of cutlery, for large deposits of both iron ore and coal outcrop in many districts adjacent to the city. Sheffield, whose inventions and research have given to the world most of the improvements in steel from early to modern times—the last important discovery being stainless steel—stands at the junction of two fairly large streams. Fed by smaller ones, these streams once provided power for water-wheels; at one period, 400 buildings were thus equipped for cutlery production.

Large towns and capital cities have, in fact, at most early periods made their own knives. Ironworkers, generally, produced them along with arms and other articles for everyday use. London, with its Cutlers' Company, which incorporates an older Cutlers' Guild, is typical, while an example of a smaller but virile one-time cutlery centre is Thaxted, Essex, which achieved a reputation for its wares in the thirteenth century. This beautiful little town to-day has its 'Cutlers' Green', an inn sign of crossed daggers, as well as a fine fourteenth-century timbered Town Hall. There is, however, now no cutlery industry at Thaxted.

Paris, Thiers and Châtellerault in France, Nuremberg, Solingen and Ramscheid in Germany, Toledo and Seville in Spain, Eskilstuna in Sweden, and Namur in Belgium had a good reputation for cutlery in medieval and later times.

Sheffield, however, appears to have concentrated on fine quality in the most important part of the knife, the blade, and gained thereby a supreme position in the world. As early as A.D. 1160, iron smelting and working were well evidenced in the district, a connection that has continued right up to the present. There is no doubt that a small amount of iron working was carried on within four miles of Sheffield Castle, on the site of a Roman fort, but except for vague references and guesses, nothing relative to the story of Sheffield cutlery has been recorded between that time and the twelfth century.

Apart from a church and a castle in the twelfth century, Sheffield can also claim the distinction of having an important Saxon Aula of Waltheof when William the Conqueror landed in England in 1066. But it is only in recent years that some of the earliest dates and names of Sheffield craftsmen have been discovered. They support the conviction of S. O. Addy, the Sheffield historian, that it was the only town besides London which had a reputation for cutlery during the period 1315 to 1531.

There is evidence, too, that some of the early Sheffield products were of more than 'provincial' quality. A knife, probably of the sixteenth century, that was found in Sheffield Castle moat not only had decorative chasing on a long octagon bolster, but was also gold-damascened. Another found at the same time had silver rivets.

Of the whittles found in Sheffield Castle moat, one measured 6 in.

D

overall, including a 'knocked-on' handle, while another was $7\frac{1}{2}$ in. in length. The blades of both had been forged out of a square or oblong section iron rod. The hardness approximated to that of modern steel knives, but the whittles were of iron, case-hardened in charcoal.

Fig. 14. Whittle from Sheffield Castle moat, *circa* fourteenth century

Another knife found in the moat had a three-pin scale-tang, and it measured $7\frac{1}{4}$ in. overall. The scales were wooden, with brass pins and silver washers. Thickest part of the blade measured $\frac{1}{7}$ in. and it was swaged on the back for $2\frac{1}{2}$ in. This knife originated from the sixteenth century.

One of the most interesting finds was part of a knife, the blade, bolster and tang of which had been forged out of a solid piece of steel. The greatest diameter of the bolster, a somewhat flattened octagon in section, was $\frac{3}{8}$ in. from back to front and $\frac{5}{16}$ in. across. The facets of the octagon were perfectly squared and ornately chased with punches. On each front and back square was worked a pattern of scrolls with leaf terminals, framed by a double-indented line. Four facets, one on each side of the front and back squares, were deeply chased, each with four deep longitudinal oval punchings, alternating with three delicately indented lines across the width of the faces. The bolster had been damascened with heavy gold on all the flat surfaces. This knife dates from either the sixteenth or seventeenth centuries.

A similar find was oval in bolster section, but was neither decorated nor gilded.

A blade (or side) of a pair of shear-shaped scissors, measuring $5\frac{7}{8}$ in. long, found at the same time, had been delicately forged. The bow measured $\frac{1}{4}$ in. and the shank $\frac{1}{12}$ in. in thickness. A slight 'set' or bend from end to end gave a rise of $\frac{1}{4}$ in. in the centre if laid horizontally. This style of shear scissors first appeared in the Iron Age (Fig. 9).

These relics date mostly from the sixteenth and seventeenth centuries, and it is noteworthy that although the ordinances of the Cutlers' Company of Hallamshire, of which district Sheffield is the centre, can be traced back to 1565, they were at that time already described as being ancient. In them are several references to 'damasking, inlaying and studding' of knives and other wares with silver and gold. It was enacted that no gold or silver was to be put on blades, bolsters or hafts of any knives, except 'such as be worth or sold for five shillings per dozen'. Among early Sheffield workers of that time there was a goldsmith, presumably a gold-beater, who possibly made thin sheet or foil for damasking, inlaying or studding.

The Earl of Shrewsbury, when writing in 1589 to Lord Burghley, said: 'Your Lordship shall receive a case of Hallamshire Whittells being such fruits as my poor country affordeth with fame throughout the realm.' It is safe to assume that the articles were of a quality suited to the social position of the recipient.

A year later, Peter Bales, a London writing master, stated in his *Writing Schoolmaster* that in the 'choyce' of a pen knife 'a right good Sheffield knife is best'.

If further evidence is needed to establish Sheffield's reputation for producing quality wares in early days, it should be noted that in 1624 two ordinances of the Cutlers' Company, dealing with the use of gold and silver on blades, bolsters and hafts, decreed 'none were to damaske, onlay or studd any knives or wares, or intermix the same with any pewter, tin, lead, brass or other counterfeit stuff, whereby any ignorant man may be induced to take the same to be silver or gold on pain' of a fine. Ten years earlier than this, in 1614, a man was fined 40s. 'for damasking of lowe priced knives with silver wire' contrary to regulation.

When it is learned that of the 375 bridegrooms who were married at Sheffield Parish Church in the years 1653 to 1660, more than half were engaged in the cutlery or kindred trades, it is certain that most of them were making goods of repute, otherwise the paternal Cutlers' Company would have had something to say. There was already a reputation to protect.

These figures extracted from the Parish Register of Marriages throw much light on the importance of the cutlery trades in comparison with other trades. Three-fifths of the bridegrooms were engaged in the cutlery and allied trades. First came the cutlers, including all those who could forge, grind and assemble, who numbered 122, or a third of the total. Next were the scissorsmiths, who accounted for forty-two; sheathers, seventeen; shearsmiths, seven; scythesmiths, three; filesmiths, three; and one hammer-man.

Most of these men carried on their crafts in 'hulls' that were situated chiefly along the waterways of Sheffield. At one time there were 400 of these hulls, or water-wheels, and one of them on the Porter Stream was adopted by the Sheffield Trades' Technical Society's Industrial Museum, and later taken over by the Corporation of Sheffield.

Nearby was a ford over which grindstones were brought from Brincliffe Edge and Wickersley quarries. The building has been identified as

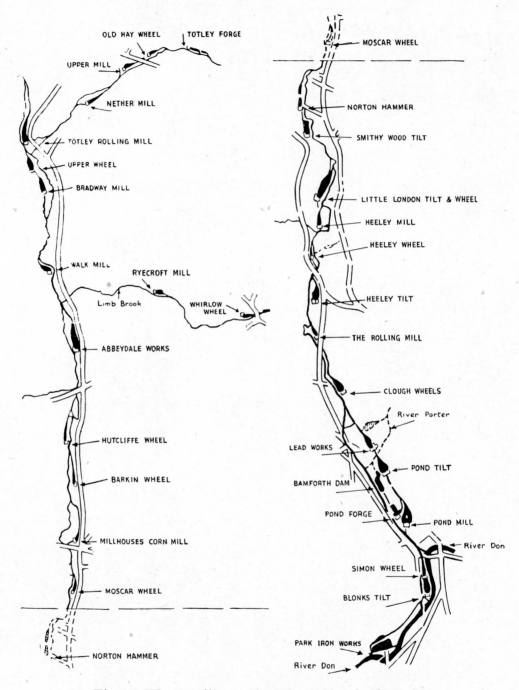

OLD HAY WHEEL   TOTLEY FORGE

MOSCAR WHEEL

UPPER MILL

NETHER MILL

NORTON HAMMER

SMITHY WOOD TILT

TOTLEY ROLLING MILL

UPPER WHEEL

BRADWAY MILL

LITTLE LONDON TILT & WHEEL

HEELEY MILL

HEELEY WHEEL

WALK MILL

RYECROFT MILL

Limb Brook   WHIRLOW WHEEL

HEELEY TILT

THE ROLLING MILL

ABBEYDALE WORKS

CLOUGH WHEELS

River Porter

HUTCLIFFE WHEEL

LEAD WORKS

POND TILT

BAMFORTH DAM

BARKIN WHEEL

POND FORGE

POND MILL

River Don

MILLHOUSES CORN MILL

SIMON WHEEL

MOSCAR WHEEL

BLONKS TILT

PARK IRON WORKS

River Don

NORTON HAMMER

Fig. 15. Water-mills on the River Sheaf, Sheffield
(From Miller's *Water-mills of Sheffield.* By courtesy of Mrs. Miller)

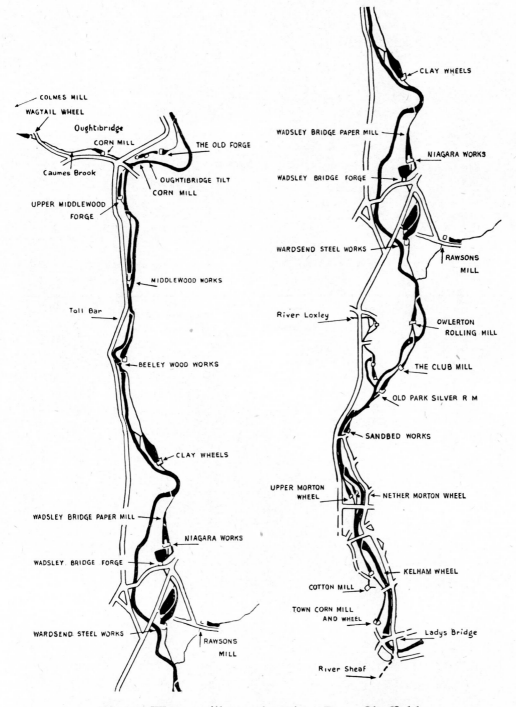

Fig. 16. Water-mills on the River Don, Sheffield
(From Miller's *Water-mills of Sheffield*. By courtesy of Mrs. Miller)

'Portar Whele' and, according to Miller's *Water-mills of Sheffield* (printed by Pawson and Brailsford)—

> it is mentioned in the will of . . . William Beighton of Stumper Lawe, cutler . . . dated 1584, which included among other legacies . . . 'To Thomas, Robte, and Hugh Beighton my sons all my interest, term, titles and possession which I have in and upon one Watter Whele called Portar Whele which I have of the grant of the said Earl' (of Shrewsbury).

Porter Wheel appears in the rent-books of the Earls of Shrewsbury from 1615 to 1637. A tenant named Shepherd occupied it in 1797, when there were ten troughs employing ten men. Three generations of the family of Hinde worked at Shepherd's Wheel, as it is now called, for 100 years. One of the most recent members of this family, W. T. Hinde, was well-known as a fine craftsman.

These old water wheels, which built up Sheffield's early reputation for quality cutlery, also contributed to two of the most important periods in the history of the trade—the years when the United States of America were being developed and later the South American boom years. The Rev. A. Gatty, in *Sheffield Past and Present* (Thos. Rodgers, Sheffield, and Bell & Sons, London, 1873), said that—

> the really first large fortunes made in Sheffield sprang from the American trade . . . within 15 or 20 years after the general peace (in 1815). Sheffield business houses had established their agents in New York before the beginning of the 19th century and immediately after the peace, America was ready to purchase all that could be supplied.

There was a mad rush for goods. During the period 1820 to 1830 the population of the United States rose from 9,638,000 to 12,866,000, a greater proportionate increase than in any previous decade of that country's history, an increase that is reflected in the amazing value of this transatlantic trade. By 1863, however, a reaction was well on the way and 'money became so scarce in America that Sheffield merchants could not obtain payment for their exported goods'.

Some patterns of Sheffield knives were known both to local cutlery people and in American markets by names, the origins of many of which have long been forgotten. A number of these names, however, have been traced to individuals or places. A pocket knife that sold in hundreds of thousands, for instance, was known as a 'Stannington Barlow', the first word indicating that it came from a village near Sheffield, while Barlow was the name of the makers, who were two brothers. 'Furness Barlows' originated later in the same district, being made by a family named Furness. As recently as sixty years ago, the Furness brothers of Stannington brought their knives into Sheffield to be packed with the goods of other manu-facturers for shipment abroad, generally to the United States, at a very low price. In *Huckleberry Finn*, Mark Twain referred to the Barlow knife from Sheffield 'worth two bits in any store'.

A well-known Sheffield pocket knife that was popular in the U.S.A. was known as the 'Congress knife', while another type made by the oldest cutlery firm in Sheffield bore the name of 'palf'. Designed by a workman named Palfreyman and made in both single and two-blade styles, it sold in thousands in the United States. It was made of the best possible material in the highest standards of craftsmanship.

The 'dadley' bolster of some table and cooks' knives was presumably also named after a man. To-day a narrow, scimitar-shaped carving knife is often called 'launder' in shape. This is a corruption of 'Lander', for a blade like it was produced in Sheffield for the American firm of Lander, Frary and Clarke.

The great quantities of Bowie knives that have been made in Sheffield demonstrate the city's close links with North America. Mostly of a high quality, they were produced for strenuous pioneering work and were originally designed by Colonel Jim Bowie of Texas. Born in 1799, Bowie devoted much of his life to fighting for the liberation of Texas from the control of Mexico. It is said that the first knife, made by Bowie himself, was forged out of an old file. The 'Bowie' became the pattern for all good hunters as well as the desperadoes of the 'Golden West'. Generally double-edged, the blade varied in length from 10 in. to 14 in. and the finest Shef-field materials and skill were used in its production. (The Bowie knife and the life of its inventor are described in Chapter 14.)

Another example of a knife for early pioneers that was produced in quantity in Sheffield was a pocket knife, which, designed for Australian markets, was deeply marked with the words 'To strike fire', the intention being to provide a means of making a fire with tinder.

About the beginning of the present century a razor made in Sheffield especially for a London firm had the inscription 'Genesis XL, verse 14,' etched in gilt on the side of the blade. It was known as the Genesis razor.

A class of knife that figured prominently in the development of colonial and other areas was the matchet. Perhaps described more correctly as a tool, the uses of the matchet varied with its size and shape: they included sugar-cane-cutting, clearing scrub and saplings from newly developed land and so on. Some patterns approximated to a sword in style, with a blade of some 30 in. in length. In countries covered with bush or forest, most of the inhabitants, even girls, carried a matchet, for defence against man and wild animals.

In the East and West Indies and South America, matchets were—and still are—used in immense quantities. Made mostly from Sheffield steel in its finer grades, many of the large sizes were produced in other edge-tool centres, such as Wolverhampton and Glasgow. Sheffield manufacturers were inclined to look upon the matchet as an edge tool, rather than an item of cutlery.

An instance of a native people's appreciation for Sheffield quality goods is provided by J. R. Ackerley in *Hindoo Holiday—an Indian Journey* (Chatto and Windus, Revised, 1952). The author wrote:

> As Babaji Rao and I were walking in the outskirts of the village this evening, two old peasants, a man and a woman, begged of me, the old woman was ill, it seemed; she squatted on the ground at my feet and moaned and rocked herself, holding out her clawlike hands, while the old man, who was thin and hairy and almost entirely naked, begged for medecine for her, 'good medecine', he kept saying, 'Rogers medecine'.
>
> Babaji was very amused, and explained to me that there were some steel articles of recognised excellence, marked 'Rogers' being sold at the fair, and the old man wanted some medecine as good as this steel.
>
> 'Of course he thinks you are a doctor', he said; 'these poor people think that all white men are doctors'.
>
> I asked him to explain that I was unfortunately not a doctor, and I gave the old man a rupee to buy some 'Rogers Medecine'.

The name of the noted Sheffield cutlery firm is 'Rodgers'—spelt, of course, with a 'd', but this extract is quoted as the author recorded it in his book.

All the details of the many kinds of knives that Sheffield cutlers have produced could not be crowded into a volume of this size. There are, for instance, thousands of trade terms, while styles and patterns have changed much during the last sixty years. Some of the names should, however, be recorded, for they form an historical record of the trade in Sheffield.

Cutlers still produce a wide range of patterns, including: table and dessert knives, carving, bread, ham, oyster and butchers' knives (including skinners and stickers); farmers', cooks', shoe, hunting, dagger and Bowie knives; tea and coffee pruners; pallet, desk and erasing knives. There is a large variety of shut knives—pen and pocket—with from one to eight blades, fleams and scribers, clasp, lock, budding, grafting and corn knives, sportsmen's and champagne knives. There is, in fact, an endless variation in the types of shut knives—with round, square and muck joints, nail-nick, long nail-nick, notch hollow, step tangs, catch sides, spear and castrating shaped blades, iron and brass webs, scales and bolsters, shadows, equal ends, round, reverse and flat backs, 'Wharncliffe' and 'Congress' shapes.

In table cutlery there are many different types of bolster—solid, run-on, shell and coddy—which have round as well as scale tangs, and which have been made in shear steel, crucible cast steel or stain-resisting steel. In hafting material, there are bone, stag, reindeer, ebony, beech, ivory, pearl, silver, grey and black buffalo, green horn, cocoa, rosewood, partridge, china, vulcanite and xylo, while some handles have been produced in real onyx, cornelian, moss agate, jasper and other semi-precious stones.

The last fifty years have seen a steady decrease in the size of cutlery generally. During that time, for instance, the table knife has been reduced from $6\frac{1}{4}$ in. in blade length with a $4\frac{1}{4}$ in. handle to a 5 in. blade and a $3\frac{3}{8}$ in. handle. The dessert knife blade now varies in length from $4\frac{3}{4}$ in. to $4\frac{1}{4}$ in., and it is interesting to note how popular has become the small tea knife. Does this trend mean that the development of more sedentary habits and occupations has reduced the size of the stomach, thereby rendering eating and the tools necessary for that purpose of lesser importance?

This tendency was taken a step further during the War of 1939–45, when to economise in effort and materials the United Kingdom Government prohibited the production and sale of full-sized table knives for the home market, but allowed their manufacture for the export trade during the latter years of the war. British households had to be content with dessert-size knives.

Many of the Sheffield cutlery firms that have been engaged in the manufacture of this 'utility' cutlery have long been established, producing goods of repute for centuries. These firms ably illustrate the qualities that have given Sheffield world renown. There are many more firms than can be mentioned in these pages, for the craft of cutlery in Sheffield has been passed from father to son in succeeding generations in scores of family concerns.

With registered trade marks dating from the year 1682, Joseph Rodgers & Sons Ltd. justify the phrase, 'a world-wide reputation for quality'. The firm was one of the few manufacturing concerns that held its own stocks of raw materials on its own premises. Its showrooms, built about 1860 in Norfolk Street, Sheffield, became a pattern for others to follow and to them came visitors, including royalty, from all parts of the world.

In 1869, Joseph Rodgers & Sons were producing each week 3,000 dozens of table knives, 1,200 dozens of pocket knives, 80 dozens of razors and 600 dozens of scissors. All these products were of the highest quality.

The works in 1878 used 26 tons of ivory for handles and scales,

Fig. 17. (Top). The first cutlery showroom opened at 6 Norfolk Street, Sheffield, by Joseph Rodgers & Sons, Ltd.
(Bottom). Shear steel making before rolling into strings

58

comprising 2,561 tusks, averaging over 22 lb. each. In about 1911, the store-room held 15 tons of ivory that was valued at some £22,000. Several of the tusks weighed about 160 lb. each, while a special tusk weighed 216 lb. Others included baby teeth, weighing only 2 or 3 lb.

Joseph Rodgers & Sons have protected their reputation for high quality by acquiring the businesses of all cutlery firms in Great Britain bearing the names of 'Rodgers' or 'Rogers'.

With its outstanding reputation for cutlery, particularly pocket knives and scissors, the old-established firm of George Wostenholm & Son Ltd. emphasised its close and early association with the American trade by naming its Sheffield premises the 'Washington Works'. This company played an important part in the development of the Bowie knife.

That part of Sheffield known as Nether Edge, where the founder of the business, George Wostenholm, made his residence, bought land and laid out tree-lined roads, giving them names such as Washington, Kenwood and Wostenholm, now forms a distinctive residential neighbourhood.

Another name that is recorded in the history of the Cutlers' Company of Sheffield, and which is also well known to-day, is that of John Ragg. Apprenticed at the age of fourteen in 1626, he appears to have been an ancestor of the present principals of J. and W. Ragg Ltd., makers of cutlery and tuning forks. There are, in fact, many other present-day Sheffield cutlers with connections dating back to ancestors whose names were recorded in the Cutlers' Company Register of Apprentices and Freemen of the early seventeenth century.

The manufacturers and craftsmen of Sheffield have established such a reputation throughout the world for their high-quality steel goods, particularly cutlery and tools, that the name 'Sheffield' has attracted the attention of many imitators.

For a long time, the Cutlers' Company of Hallamshire has made strenuous efforts to uphold its contention that the use of the name 'Sheffield' in connection with metal goods must and can only mean 'Sheffield, England'.

In addition to registering the word 'Sheffield' as a community trade mark in England, the United States of America, Chile, the Argentine, India, Bolivia and elsewhere, the Cutlers' Company, in the reports of its Advisory Committee, has shown that representations on the subject have been made to the appropriate authorities—and at times legal action taken—in Germany, the United States, Japan, India, Argentina, Uruguay and other countries. A number of actions are still pending decisions in 1953.

Cutlers in Sheffield to-day, as were their ancestors, are aware of the need to maintain their reputation for high-quality wares and a recent development has been the voluntary action of the Sheffield Cutlery Manufacturers' Association in forming the Cutlery Research Council. Most of the funds of the Council, which began technical operations early in 1952, are provided by the association, but there is a contribution from the Department of Scientific and Industrial Research.

The Council's object is to carry out research work on behalf of the members of the manufacturers' association and the results are passed on to all the members. Committees drawn from the various sections of the trade decide what problems should be studied and guide the work as it proceeds.

Research in hand in the summer of 1953 included work on the properties and composition of stainless steel for cutlery, methods of producing blanks, development of mechanical aids to production and the investigation of manufacturing problems. Special attention is given to possible new methods.

Interesting developments are expected from this research work, for it is the first time that the master cutlers of Sheffield have combined their resources to seek improvements in raw materials and production processes.

WORKMEN
(FORGERS, GRINDERS, CUTLERS)
AND THEIR RAW MATERIALS
AND MEMORIALS

CHAPTER 4

WORKMEN (FORGERS, GRINDERS, CUTLERS) AND THEIR RAW MATERIALS AND MEMORIALS

WORKING hours in Sheffield seventy years ago were long; conditions were arduous and wages low. On Mondays, the working hours were from 8 a.m. to 5 p.m.; Tuesdays, from 8 a.m. to 6 p.m.; Wednesdays, Thursdays and Fridays, from 7 a.m. to 7 p.m.; and on Saturdays from 7 p.m. to 1 p.m.

About this time, George Jowitt, a grinder of pocket knife and pruner blades, disturbed by the effect of the conditions and wages on his fellow workers, concluded that changes were not only necessary, but were also possible. As I explain later in this chapter, he helped to introduce in Sheffield the artificial grinding wheel. This development effected great improvements in working conditions, for in the early 1880's many of the 'hulls' or grinding shops had unglazed windows in both summer and winter, and the floors and walls, as well as the men themselves, were covered with swarf—a mixture of wet stone and iron dust. Grinders' silicosis, asthma, rheumatism and other diseases were common.

When a young man was 'loose'—that is, when he had reached the age of twenty-one, having been apprenticed, probably as early as thirteen—his wage might be as low as 20s. a week. If trade were good and the young man was proficient, a good master might pay him 27s. or 30s. a week. Well-established workmen could possibly earn from 36s. to 40s. a week with a good firm. Out of their wages, they paid 4s. a week for trough, or 'trow', rent and power. Gas was charged to them at a rate of 3s. 6d. a quarter.

Workmen also had to provide their own tools, horsing (seat), grindstones, leather belting, bear stakes (the wooden blocks used to guide the belts), axles and working materials, such as emery, glue, beeswax, racing irons to turn the stones true, and so on. They were also responsible for repairs to their tools.

To make his grindstones, a pocket blade grinder would pay 2s. 6d. for

63

a 'cowk'—that is, the centre of a table-blade grinder's stone after it had been worked down from about 5 ft. in diameter to some 22 in. The pocket blade grinder would split this 'cowk' round the periphery with a hammer and chisel, thus providing two stones, each measuring about 3–4 in. across the face, which might last him about a week. After they had been worn down to a diameter of 12–14 in., he would sell them for 2d. to 6d. each to a razor grinder, who made his small stones for hollow grinding by breaking the larger stones into several pieces.

These pieces were then roughly hacked into a round shape and, with an axle hole pecked in the centre, were raced—or trued—with a racing steel down to a circle approximately 5 in. in diameter while revolving dry. This method of racing and the preliminary dry grinding process that was

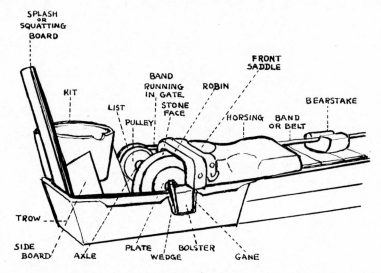

Fig. 18. Grindstone for small work on scissors, pocket knives and razors

necessary for shaping all steel tools and cutlery filled the workshop with a heavy cloud of stone and iron particles that covered the walls and lodged in every crevice. By breathing this dust into their lungs, the workmen often contracted 'grinders' disease'—silicosis. Accumulations of stone dust taken from a grinder's lungs at a *post mortem* were sometimes as large as small pearl barley.

Once or twice a week, the grinders had to 'fey' the trow—that is, remove the swarf or sludge in buckets—which is some indication of the amount of stone that was used.

Emery wheels, which worked more effectively than natural sandstones obtained from the local quarries at Wickersley and Brincliffe, were observed by George Jowitt in the 1880's being used by engineers to fettle and fashion castings. These synthetic wheels, however, were not precise enough for cutlery grinding. They did not run for long in water, as they were cold-bonded with rubber or shellac; neither would they cut keenly when run in water. They could not be used in a dry state, for that would cause knife blades to become hot and thereby lose their tempering.

In about 1906 a Continental cutler settled in Sheffield, and with George Jowitt made cold-bonded stones for engineering and general dry grinding, but little progress was made with the development of wet grinding with emery wheels.

Mr. Jowitt later heard from his brother in the United States of the use there of emery wheels that not only ran in water, but which could also stand up to twelve or eighteen months' wear, maintaining a satisfactory 'cut'. Contact was made with an agent for sales in England, who was, incidentally, meeting with great prejudice from local grinders, and a vitrified wheel that had a diameter of 28 in. with a $3\frac{1}{2}$-in. face was obtained at a cost of £6 or £7. It ran at about 5,000 surface ft. per minute, and after two weeks' trial was pronounced perfectly satisfactory. The users of quarried stone were astonished at the small wastage in the new type of wheel; only after twelve months' use had it been reduced to 14 in. in diameter. The working speed was somewhat disconcerting, for grinders were accustomed to working at about 3,600 ft. per minute.

Eventually, the advantages of quicker production, greater precision in grinding, cleanliness in operation and the fact that less pressure was required won the day against all prejudice. One factor, however, still remained unsolved—the initial cost to men without capital slowed the demand for the new wheels. Jowitt overcame this by fitting emery wheels in the grinders' hulls and accepting small payments until the men had liquidated their debts.

Jowitt became agent for the importers, but following the rising demand he later went into the manufacture of the wheels himself, establishing a lucrative business, into which he ultimately took his sons as partners. His business activities did not prevent him from leading a full life in other spheres. A sportsman of both local and national repute, Jowitt managed with the help of others to purify amateur cycling of the professional and betting elements that threatened to ruin it. He cycled from the early days—about 1886—when the cyclist was a butt for the pedestrian to assault and not too sure of police protection. At eighty-three years of age, in August, 1949, he rode tandem with a man of sixty-three from Land's End to John o' Groats with an average run of sixty miles a day, covering a total distance of 870 miles.

E

George Jowitt, whom I came to know after his partial retirement, was a man of shrewd but generous common sense, whose school had been his daily round; his schoolmaster, experience.

The grinding and finishing of all kinds of cutlery were highly specialised jobs, and the grinder typified in the mind of Sheffielders almost all that was unique in the trade. Concentrated upon him were many of the stories and jokes of over 100 years of local literature, most of which was written in the Sheffield dialect.

In the days before artificial wheels began to supersede grindstones of natural sandstone—about 1882—his colourful appearance in clothes covered with 'wheel swarf' of a brilliant yellow, caused by the iron and stone mud produced by his wet grinding processes, his strange speech, general ability to joke and indulge in rough horseplay with his fellows, and an unconcealed suspicion of people whom he did not know personally, attracted the attention of strangers to Sheffield.

The grinder had a great love of sport and recreations, such as gardening, fishing in the local streams and dams, prize-fighting, racing and following the beagles on foot. His hound lived with him in his cottage-home as one of the family. In a period when prowess in beer consumption was proverbial, the Sheffield grinder had no peer. There were, however, many grinders of quite different character, being either musical or fairly well read.

Although badly housed, poorly paid and often unintelligently fed, the grinder's high quality of craftsmanship has never been surpassed.

The grinder had a slight disdain of the forger and working cutler, who assembled the parts of a knife. He would charge the forger with making it necessary to put in extra effort to correct bad workmanship, while he dismissed the cutler with the nickname of 'fash-rag'.

Conversely, the forger and cutler weighed up the grinder and found him wanting on occasion. They said that a grinder was less than a man, and often related the story of the boy who, when asked where his father was, said: 'He's darn't t'gardin wi' two men an a groinder'! In spite of all this, it can be repeated that, at its best, the workmanship of Sheffield's grinders between the years 1790 to 1914 has never been excelled.

A high percentage of grinders were subject to chest diseases, particularly silicosis. Many of them died as a result and were, it is interesting to note, buried with their grinding wheels used as gravestones. William Hobson, for instance, who died in 1815, had inscribed on his gravestone in Sheffield Cathedral yard this epitaph:

> Beneath this a grinder lies
> A sudden death hath closed his eyes
> He lost his life by the breaking of a stone
> We hope his soul to Heaven's gone.

In the same churchyard is buried 'John Justin, senior, who dyed Feb. ye 23, 1731 aged 51 years, who was razor maker to King George ye Second'.

Two grinding stones that had been used as grave slabs were lying in St. Paul's Churchyard, Sheffield, when the church was demolished in 1936. One stone was badly eroded, so that only the date 1743 could be clearly seen. This stone had no axle and was, doubtless, quarried as a 'whittening' stone from the local Brincliffe quarries. The other stone had a square hole in the centre and on it were incised the letters 'M K'. I was allowed to have both of these stones removed to the Industrial Museum in the Endcliffe Woods.

In Attercliffe Old Chapel Yard there is a grinding stone which, measuring 20 in. in diameter, bears two inscriptions: 'I C 1776' (or, probably, 1716) and 'H. R. 1789'. Another grindstone dated 1818 was discovered in the Cathedral yard, but it has since disappeared. It was to the memory of George Hustler.

An epitaph at Norton, near Sheffield, commemorating Mark Tyzack, who died in 1795 aged seventy-one, reads:

> My scythe and hammer lie reclin'd
> My bellows too has lost his wind
> My iron is spent my steel is gone
> My scythes are set my work is done
> My fire's extinct my forge decayed
> My body in the dust is laid.

To anyone conversant with local history, this conjures up the days when individual craftsmen lived in the country around Sheffield, in close contact with rural surroundings.

In 1854, Joseph Rodgers & Sons had fixed on a wall in their factory in Norfolk Street a stone commemorating 'Joseph Whittington grinder who by correct taste united by rare skill as a workman enhanced the fame of Sheffield in its staple manufactures. Numerous specimens of his workmanship are in the show-rooms of Joseph Rodgers & Sons. His private worth equalled his skill as an artisan and this tablet has been erected to his memory by his fellow workmen in token of their estimation of his character and abilities, 1854'.

Quarried at Brincliffe, this stone would be of the same material as the grindstones of that period. Upon what article Joseph Whittington exercised his skill as a grinder no one knows. In 1943, the stone was set up against a wall in the factory yard at Pond Hill. To this day the finely cut lettering shows no sign of decay.

Much could be written of the steady, reliable and more intelligent workers in the Sheffield cutlery industry, who organised groups of fellow workmen for the improvement of their conditions and to provide material help in times of need.

Filesmiths and cutlers had formed a society or club by the year 1732. In 1748, the grinders followed on similar lines, and by 1791 scissorsmiths had done the same. In many cases, sick pay and funeral expenses were allowed to members. In 1796, thirty-six of these clubs arranged to march in procession to the opening ceremony of the Sheffield Infirmary.

In the same year, there occurred the first organised strike of a whole trade. The masters then decided to act in unison in rejecting all the demands that had been made by the men. They also refused employment to any journeyman-worker unless he produced consent in writing from his previous employer.

It was in the year 1773 that the masters, with considerable success, began to organise themselves into associations, and by 1790 manufacturers in the scissors trade formed a committee to prosecute all grinders and other workmen 'who had entered into unlawful combination to raise the price of labour'. They succeeded in getting five grinders sent to prison.

Conditions were not always so unhappy between the divergent interests, but it has been left to the present time to bridge the gap by such schemes as co-partnership, Government controls or ownership, and trades board committees, backed at times by national law and not just by local custom.

An interesting example of a nineteenth-century dispute in the trade is provided by the following letter written in 1847 by the Committee of Pearl Scale Cutters and Grinders (who were concerned at the employment of boys and men who had not served an apprenticeship) to Mabbot and Mawson, pearl scale cutters, Duke's Works, Division Street, Sheffield:

> It is always a lamantable circumstance when the employer and employed are at varanse & nothing but a seance of our duty to all connected with the Trade would induce us to address you upon your present proceador believing as we do that you are adopting measuers that will produce the most lamentable results not only to us but to yourselves and all connected. We are confident that if you will but carefulley consider the Naturel results of such steps has you are taking you will see that they will recoil with severity upon your selves. It is an indisputable fact that an over pluss of laboures his injuires to

Fig. 19. (*Top*). Boring and pinning scales on butchers' knives
(*Bottom*). Double-handed forging of butchers' knife blades in Sheffield

an inconceiveable extent to all concerned. And we cannot but think that you are ignorent of the real possition of the men and their relative possition with the Marsters or you would not so act. We would call your attention to the fact that their his at the present only 12 men partiecaley employed two of which are on warning without prospect of a situation & there is 6 men without imployment at all his not this a deplorable state of things, one third of those dependant upon the Trade for their support unable to obtain work at it is a state of things which calls upon all connected with it to inquire carefully into the cause and if possible to amend it. Our Trade is plased under particular sorcumstances in the production of its demand, circumstances which we can neither create nor control all that we can do benefishly his to reguleate the amount of labour to the demand. If the labourers be above the demand the results are destitution to the men has his evident by the fact above stated out of 18 men 6 out of imployment then comes the enquirey how his this—it his self evident. Hands have been introduced at a greater rate of increase than the amount of labour warrents then to go on introducing fresh Hands will end in those who are but about half employed at the present would soon have nothing. In what possition do the men now stand to the Marsters. If you are to go on introducing boys and men who have not served their time to the trade we shall like the 6 preseding us be driven from our imployment & we must either seek imployment at a fresh trade at a great sacrifice go on the Parish—or commence Marsters ourselves & we leave it your own Judgement (looking at the men) which his the most likely. Then look at the result. Just the same has in the former so in the latter. Has the introduction of Boy has thrown out of imployment the men so the introduction of New Marsters will pull down the Profits of the Imployer so we go on untill all his one mass of Ruin. Has not this been the case your own experience will corroberate that has new Marster have sprong up the prices have come down. We call your attention to the fact. We do not wish to dictate neither to you nor anyone else how you are to manage your business. But we do think we have no right to sit & see the Bread taken from our Mouth & no effort to prevent it more so that we should be made a Help mete to it.

We therefore respectfull lay these consideration before you & in Conclution would inform you that some of the Trade will in a few days wait upon you so that you may confer together upon the important subject of introducing Boy into the Trade.   (*In the collection of the Author.*)

There are to-day a large number of educationalists who desire to raise the school leaving age to seventeen years, but in the nineteenth century the cutlery trade was no exception to the general use in industry of juvenile labour. In 1911, Joseph Rodgers & Sons published a list of thirty-six of their workmen who had completed fifty years' service or more with the firm. There were seven with fifty years' service, two with fifty-one years, two with fifty-two years, four with fifty-three, four with fifty-four, four with fifty-five, two with fifty-six, five with fifty-seven, one with fifty-eight, three with sixty, and one each with sixty-one and sixty-two years of service with the company.

Three of these workpeople were seventy-three years old in 1911, while three of them had started work at nine years of age and eight of them at ten to eleven years.

Many of these workmen were no doubt well versed in the local Sheffield dialect, which differed considerably from the dialects of other parts of Yorkshire. In Abel Bywater's *The Sheffield Dialect*, published in 1839 (Houston), there is a reliable account of 'ivvera thing ats dun to a pen knoife throot furst tot last'.

Wa then o'st begin wit blade makker furst:
1st. He mood'st blade.
2nd. Then he tangs it.
3rd. Then he smithies it.
4th. Then he hardens an tempers it, an he's dun we't. Wa then heast spring makker:
1st. He moods it.
2nd. Then he draws tuther end aht an turns it, an's just as menna he'ats fort scale; wa then't blade gooas tot wheel tubbe grun an sich loik.
1st. Nah, thah kno's, we alis groind tang furst, fort mark to be struckn, but ivverra bodda dus'nt.
2nd. Then groindt blade.
3rd. If its a rahnd ended knoife, tangs is glazed and pollisht.
4th. Then they'r choil'd if they'r not fetheredged ans.
5th. Then they'r grun uppat droi stooan.
6th. Swages is glazed, and backs, if they'r tubbe pollisht.
7th. Wa then they'r lapt.
8th. An then pollisht, an then he's dun we't.
Then heast Cutler's wark al bit warst, bur o think o can mannidge.
1st. He sets scales tot plate.
2nd. Bores t'scales.
3rd. Foiles an fits em.
4th. Nocks em aht an marks springs.
5th. Rahnds springs, an hardens an tempers em.
6th. Then he rasps an sets his cuverin.
7th. Then he matches an pins em on.
8th. Tak's em dahn an dresses t'edges.
9th. Nocks em aht an scrapes t'edges at iron scales.
10th. Puts springs intot hefts.
11th. Squar'st blades an dresses em.
12th. Nails em in joints an sets em.
13th. If they'r stag they want heftin.
14th. (missed out).
15th. Foils't bowsters.
16th. Ruff buffs t'hefts.
17th. Ruff glazes't bowsters.
18th. Then woips sand off.

19th. Foin buffs em we oil an rottenston.

20th. Foin glazest bowsters.

21st. Then glosses em off an they'r finsht, arnt they, Jooa?

Jooa: 'Nou lad, not sooa, thahs mist two things. Thah'l loise (wager) if ta dusnt moind.'

Jooa Crocus: 'Wa o can think o nowt else. Wot have a mist, eh?'

Jooa: 'Dusn't thah know at after't springs is hardened an temper'd, theyr glaz'd an burnisht; an at after he matches an pins em on, he nips em an bores't thick horn hoils, an puts points in?'

Jooa Crocus: 'Wa mun o did'nt owt to loise for that bit; bur, o avver, let's just reckon hah menny toimes won part or anuther on em gooas throo us hands.'

Jooa: 'Wa then, we'll begin wit blade makker, furst:

Blade Makker	toimes	4
Scale an Spring Makker	toimes	4
Groinder	toimes	8
Cutler or Setters in	toimes	23
	total	39

besoids a menna mooar little jobs, stitch as wettin an woipin, etc.'

Sheffield's cutlery industry has during its long history, which stretches through many centuries, inspired a number of radical changes both in the raw materials used and in methods of production; changes that subsequently were adopted by cutlers throughout the world. When new ideas were introduced, however, they usually met with prejudice, for Sheffield craftsmen had first to be convinced that established practices could be bettered.

Although, for instance, Benjamin Huntsman invented crucible steel in Sheffield in about 1742—a discovery which revolutionised steel-making all over the world and which is still the basis of all modern methods of making high-class steel—his own countrymen did not take too kindly to it at first. Crucible steel was much harder and finer in texture than the steel they were used to handling, and it required a new technique and skill. It is recorded, however, that cast steel razors were made in February 1771, while in January 1772, polished razors, marked 'acier fondu', were being made in Sheffield in the new steel for the South American market.

Orders for cutlery and tools were also executed in the new steel in 1775 for shipment to Hamburg. These goods were forged from 'strings' of steel rolled from the cast ingot. They should not be confused with cast articles of a common quality, which are sometimes referred to as steel, but which are actually of cast iron and worthless in use.

There have been a number of other radical changes in the Sheffield cutlery trade, particularly with the greater application of scientific research during, say, the last seventy years.

From time immemorial wood, stag antler and the horn of the buffalo and the domestic oxen have, with ivory, tortoiseshell and pearl, been used extensively for the hafting of cutlery. As the Industrial Revolution spread through Western Europe and the United States, Sheffield became a centre that not only absorbed vast quantities of these hafting materials, but which also exported them on a considerable scale, either in a partly prepared state or as semi-manufactured material. Merchants in Germany, France and the United States found that the experienced craftsmen of Sheffield could even buy raw material in the open markets of the world, cut it into sizes for handling and then offer it for re-export at better terms than if they had done the job themselves.

Wilmot Taylor in his *Sheffield Horn Industry* (J. W. Northend, Sheffield, 1927), said that at the dawn of the nineteenth century horn dealers and pressers monopolised the centre of Sheffield for their trade. He estimated that in about 1887 'the output of four to five-hundred gross (72,000) of stag handles and scales would be a weekly contribution to the needs of the cutlery industry'.

The number of firms in Sheffield and district in 1850 who dealt in raw materials for handling totalled 145, 'no doubt employing', said Taylor, 'well over a thousand hands'. Wilmot Taylor's own concern, acting as agents for London dealers, had in 1872 '122 tons [of ivory] in their cellars and stockrooms in Sheffield'. Their books showed 'sales of ivory tusks as over £6,000 in value for the month of November 1872'.

These particulars of ivory, a high-priced material, suggest that much larger quantities of cheaper materials, such as wood, bone and horn, were used for lower-priced and mass-produced cutlery. It was, in fact, a reasonably common sight—and one well within my recollection—to see truck loads of black buffalo horns passing through the streets of Sheffield, having arrived from the United States.

Handles were first made in synthetic materials in about 1870, a few years after two English workers, Alexander Parkes and Daniel Spill, succeeded in producing a material suitable for handles. Early synthetic handles were known by names such as crayford and fictile ivory, xylonite and zilonoid, all of which were imitations of ivory, but lacking its pleasing appearance. In 1868, John Hyatt first made Celluloid in commercial quantities by treating cotton with nitric acid and camphor. Celluloid had a more satisfactory tint and quality than other synthetic hafting material, and after a time it ousted bone, horn, ebony and rosewood, leaving only a slight demand for table cutlery handles, pocket knife scales and razor scales of ivory or pearl. To minimise the shrinkage in size and weight which is a characteristic of the material, Celluloid was sometimes kept for two years in a warm chamber. In more recent times, this seasoning period has been much reduced.

In 1947 it was estimated that 24,000,000 handles in Celluloid were needed annually to meet the demands of Sheffield table knife cutlers.

Historical periods in manufacturing methods in Sheffield may be marked by the following developments:

(1) When workers gave up using the foot treadle in their homes as a means of obtaining power and turned to water wheels on the streams that ran through the local valleys. Some grinding 'hulls' existed early in the sixteenth century, and possibly earlier.

(2) The introduction of steam power and erection of factories, enticed workers into the town from their small holdings in nearby hamlets and villages, where they had been self-supporting, possessing their own tools and working under healthy rural conditions. The first steam-power factories in Sheffield were built about 1786. Gas engines came on to the scene early in the nineteenth century, but they gave way fairly quickly with the advent of electric motors, which distributed power and light most effectively in both small and large concerns.

(3) Machine forging, or 'goffing', which was developed about 1880, together with mechanised grinding methods, almost superseded hand work for the heavy initial processes of cutlery making by the beginning of the twentieth century.

(4) The introduction of stainless, or stain-resisting, steel in 1914 ultimately ousted shear and carbon steel for table cutlery, making the triumph of machine and mass production more certain, for the new steel could not readily be forged by hand.

(5) An important development of the late nineteenth century was the introduction of emery and abrasive grindstones for all methods of grinding in the cutlery trade. As I have already mentioned, George Jowitt, a local grinder who acted as agent for the United States firm that first brought them into use, ultimately made them himself and thereby amassed a small fortune.

Stainless steel for cutlery was introduced in 1914 through the discoveries and experimental work of Harry Brearley of Sheffield. Its advent met with the opposition that was usually meted out by masters, workmen and users when faced with a new development.

The steel was different in many ways from what they had been accustomed to handling. Firstly, it was not possible to forge it by hand in the way that best-quality table cutlery was then being made; stainless steel had to be goffed by machine hammer.

It was similar in character to self-hardening steel, and did not react readily to the usual hardening and tempering methods of quenching and reducing by gradual reheating to 'draw' the hardness down a little. Neither the structure nor the composition of the metal gave the results for which for generations the forgers and the grinders manipulating the older shear and carbon steels had looked.

During the transition from the old to the new form of steel, manufacturers found it difficult to keep the rough blades of carbon steel knives separate from those of stainless steel—there was so little difference in general appearance. Some of the troubles that arose from this accidental mixing of the two types can readily be imagined. Grinders were no better disposed towards the change when they found that the new steel did not grind so readily upon the stones then in use, for the different composition clogged the surface of their grindstones.

Most people when they first contacted a knife made of stainless steel felt that it was up to them to subject it to every possible test, either reasonable or unreasonable, such as no knife could ever be expected to meet in domestic or other service. An unfounded story was spread to the effect that anyone receiving a cut from a stain-resisting steel knife would find a virulent poison at work. Jewellers tested the stain-resisting quality of the new steel with *aqua regia*, ignoring the fact that it had been produced chiefly to withstand domestic food acids. These prejudices, coupled with the dislocation of trade that followed the outbreak of the First World War in August of the same year, meant that stainless steel cutlery was slow to attain its rightful place.

Another popular fallacy that arose was not solely based upon prejudice and ignorance. It was said that stain-resisting steel would not cut so well as the older type of knife. Difficulties in tempering during the experimental period had resulted in some of the early stainless steel knives being left heavy and thick after grinding, to counteract a slight softness and to prevent bending. To some extent this affected the sharpness. In addition, the old type of steel knife had the advantage that frequent cleaning on a knife board or in a rotary brush machine tended to sharpen the blade by thinning it. There was, however, no need to clean the new steel, and constant pressure on the hard surface of porcelain plates tended to blunt the edge, making an occasional sharpening a necessity.

After these difficulties had been overcome, and as soon as there was a demand for the new cutlery, the buyers of many large distributing firms began a process that is not unusual under a system of competitive trading.

They tried to pull prices down to the level of the former style of knife. To secure their large orders, producing firms cut each others' prices. Low selling prices ultimately resulted in lower wages, and the grinder, finding that he could not make a reasonable living, left out a good deal of his best effort. About the same time, grinding by machinery was introduced and in places it was adapted for boy and girl labour. At once, qualities that had been regarded as a *sine qua non* both by manufacturers and workers in building up the reputation of Sheffield cutlery became of secondary importance to many in the hurry and scurry of mass production. In this trend away from high quality, they were aided and abetted by the inventions of twentieth-century engineers.

Those reputable makers who tried to produce a good stainless knife with all the cutting qualities of the carbon steel found that conditions were beyond their control. They were compelled either to carry on a small trade at fairly remunerative prices or to supply medium qualities to meet the demand for low, competitive, prices.

Soon after the close of the Great War, with my wife and daughter, I visited Italy, staying at the Hotel Wagner on the Lido, Venice. My statement that a knife which I showed to the hotel manager was rustless and stainless was too extraordinary to be believed. The knife was stuck into a lemon and left in the manager's possession for twenty-four hours. At the end of that time, the manager was so surprised by the result that he took the knife to a meeting of his confrères who had not before seen stain-resisting cutlery—but seeing was believing. A week or two later, I had a similar experience in Florence when the knife was shown to a cutlery maker there who was producing knives for cutting pineapples on plantations.

Sheffield was not only the birthplace of stainless steel for cutlery, but also of most of the other major developments within the cutlery trade throughout the world. It is not certain, however, whether any other cutlery-making centre can claim to have been established before Sheffield, unless it is the City of London. The Worshipful Cutlers' Company of London may be associated with the Cutlery Guild of that city which in 1298, it is recorded, sought to stamp out illegal trading. Although the output of cutlery produced in London may have been large in the past when compared with Continental cities, it has for many years steadily declined. During Victorian times, London's imports of raw materials for cutlery making and her exports of finished cutlery must have exceeded those of any other port in the world.

The Sheffield Cutlers' Company was incorporated by an Act of

Parliament in 1624 and invested with powers 'for the good order and government of makers of knives, scissors, shears, sickles and other cutlery wares in Hallamshire'—that is, the district surrounding Sheffield. There is a certain amount of evidence that this Company, or Guild, was incorporated some hundreds of years after Sheffield cutlery had gained more than a local reputation. In the previous chapter, for instance, there is a reference to 'Cuttelum de Shefeld' in an inventory concerning the Royal Wardrobe of the Tower of London. That was within the period 1272–1327.

OLD AND OBSOLETE PROCESSES OF CUTLERY DECORATION

CHAPTER 5

OLD AND OBSOLETE PROCESSES OF CUTLERY DECORATION

FOR hundreds of years, craftsmen have coloured metals by heat treatment and by thin plating, either for decorative effect or to give base substances the appearance of more valuable materials. This was particularly so in the East—ancient Egypt and Assyria, for instance, have provided many examples of this practice. Metal workers in ancient Greece plated coins of base metal with scarcer material, thus anticipating, in principle, the nineteenth-century process known as Old Sheffield Plate.

The line distinguishing the deceptive from the decorative and the colouring of metals for utility purposes is often very fine. This subject, involving ethical, philosophical and utilitarian considerations, has un-limited ramifications, but it can be narrowed down if kept within the bounds of what has occurred in Sheffield during the last seventy years.

In a very few years, time, it will be impossible to make this record of obsolete processes of decorating cutlery, for the hand craftsman and industrial artist seem to be fast disappearing in the face of engineering mass production, in which little of the skill and taste of the old order is reflected.

During the nineteenth- and early twentieth-centuries, when small workshops and the cottage houses of the workers abutted on to the streets, passers-by could stand and watch Sheffield's craftsmen-decorators at work. Much of their craft was often executed without the aid of mechanical power; for instance, file cutting on the underside of razor tangs to give a thumb grip, or the whetting—final sharpening—of the fine edges of razor blades, pocket knives and surgical instruments, the filing and burnishing of scissor shanks and bows and the assembly, or putting together, of scissors.

Many of these processes were carried on at home by housewives in between their normal household duties. Artistic crafts, such as engraving and chasing and both flat and round *repoussé*—the latter gave a final finish to ornamental cast non-ferrous work and called more for skill with simple tools than with motive power—were often carried on in the living-room, probably the only room on the ground floor. For the hand forging of razors, pocket blades, scissors or table blades, the working cutler for a shilling or two a week could rent a small workshop adjoining his house, or in a backyard.

Rather than enter large factories, hundreds of people worked in these conditions in Sheffield, Birmingham and other industrial towns, or their suburbs. Even about 100 years after the building of steam-powered factories in which tenements with motive power laid-on could be rented (*circa* 1786), workers could often be seen performing in their own homes light manufacturing processes, such as polishing with a pedal lathe.

Until these steam power factories were first erected, grinding, both light and heavy, was effected by water power in the 'hulls' that were built as early as 1500 on the banks of the streams that run into Sheffield from the north, west and south. When the workers gave up their grinding hulls, they carried on their work in the steam factories of the towns, using the same tools and employing the same methods.

Before the arrival of stainless steel, shear or cast steel cutlery, after rough grinding on natural stone or artificial wheels, was treated to a finer grade of grinding. This was effected by glazing on wooden wheels, covered with glued-on hard leather that was dressed with powdered emery mixed with glue. Fine emery mixed with melted suet and applied to the glazed surface completed the finish.

When stainless steel was introduced in 1914, it was found that the higher the polish it could be given, the greater was its resistance to stain or corrosion. A compound, incorporating chrome—already used as an ingredient in the steel—was applied by a felt wheel, or rag dolly, to produce a mirror polish.

Bread knife handles displayed some fine styles of carving, particularly those made of ivory. The technique and the material called for the use of

Fig. 20. English and Continental decorated cutlery

(*Top*). Part of a set of 12 knives, the ivory handles being carved with figures of the apostles—James, Mark, Matthew, Paul, Philip and John. From the Sanders Fiske collection of about 200 pieces of English and Continental antique cutlery. They were presented to the Sheffield Public Museum by the National Art-Collections Fund.

(*Bottom*). Seventeenth- and eighteenth-century cutlery—left to right: miniature shears of French origin (*circa* 1620); knife and fork, painted enamel of Dutch origin (*circa* 1780); engraved silver wedding knife and fork of Dutch origin (*circa* 1620); enamelled wedding knife and fork with gold and rubies, of Dutch origin (*circa* 1650); three pieces of seventeenth-century German miniature ivory.

(These items are in the collection at the Sheffield City Museum.)

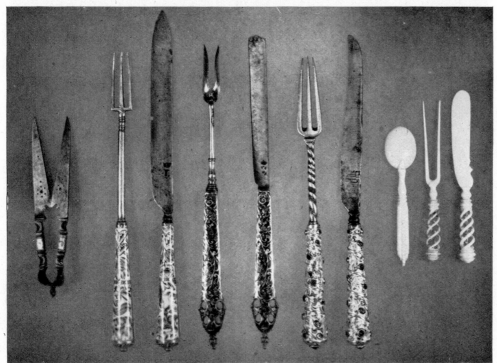

(By courtesy of the Sheffield City Museum)

very small hand tools as fine as those used to-day by the average engraver when cutting monograms on silver. Early in the nineteenth century ivory fluters, as these workers were called, made their own tools. Such fine work is no longer executed for commercial purposes. Bread knives of a lower standard were fitted with cheaply carved boxwood or sycamore handles (Fig. 29).

Fruit-dessert knives and forks, fish eaters and fish carvers had handles carved in the same manner as ivory and pearl bread knives. In the eighteenth and nineteenth centuries, dessert knives and forks were made of steel and close plated, as were some fish knives and forks of the nineteenth century. After the process of depositing electro-plate on nickel silver was introduced in the latter part of the nineteenth century, fish blades and forks were often saw-pierced with a pattern, as well as being engraved. This was not the case with fruit eaters, which were engraved only (Figs. 21 and 22).

Soon after the advent of stainless steel, fruit-desserts and fish eaters were being produced in the new metal, but they were no longer ornamented with engravings or flat chasing.

Pocket and pen knives of the nineteenth century were produced in thousands of different patterns to suit many purposes and were the subject of much decorative craftsmanship, chiefly at the hands of the grinder and the working cutler. The handles of these knives were made of bone, horn, ivory, pearl, silver and gold; materials which called for skilful treatment at the hands of the decorator.

From the period of the Roman occupation have come pocket knives that were made with large blades only and with no springs. The smaller pen blade was not produced until much later, when it was made for the scribe to trim his quill pen—a delicate operation. The cutting quality of these fine blades was largely dependent on thin grinding and careful finishing. From the seventeenth century to the beginning of the twentieth century, it is probable that more thought and care was bestowed on the manufacture of pen knives than on any other article of cutlery.

Fig. 21. Silver and electro-plated fruit-dessert knives

These patterns include knives with pearl and metal handles. Ferrules are of silver, and blades, while most of the bolsters are ornate. Many of the blades are either engraved or chased.

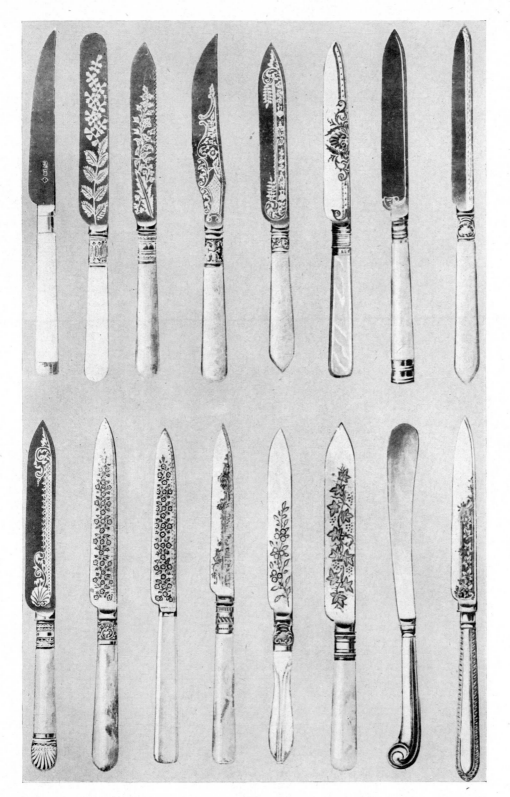

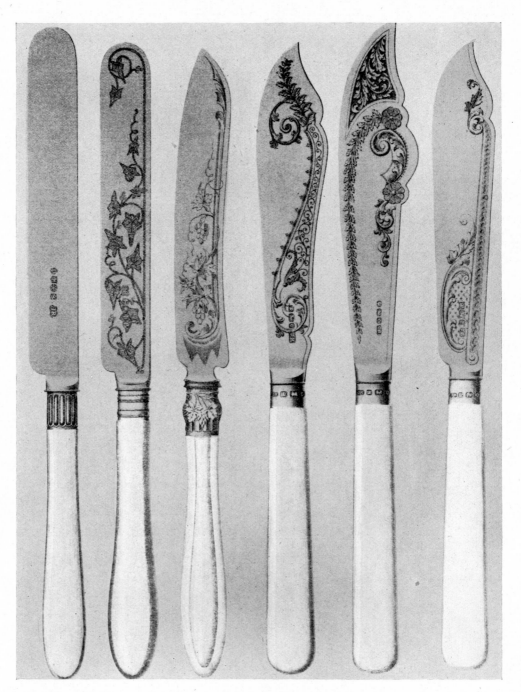

Fig. 22. Fruit-dessert knives and fish eaters

The first three knives are fruit-desserts, the other three being fish knives. Blades are either of sterling silver or plated on steel. Some are chased, while other designs are engraved. Handles are of ivory or pearl.

Fine workmanship and variety of pattern deteriorated during the First World War and to-day comparatively few designs are available, because mechanised mass production now rules the cutlery trade throughout the world. Shortly after the turn of the present century, cutlery craftsmen were called on to join the armed forces or to work in munition factories. Apprentices were no longer being trained in the manufacture of knives for civilian users.

Although most of the pen and pocket knives illustrated in Figs. 40, 42, 44 and 45, belong to the eighteenth and nineteenth centuries, that shown top row, fifth from left in Fig. 46 is typical of the patterns produced for the average user for some years after the end of the 1939–45 War. Even that, however, was not readily obtainable.

Pen and pocket knife blades were not made in stainless steel until some time after it had been adopted for table cutlery. Ultimately the whole of the knife-blades, and the springs and scales were produced in the new steel.

Before synthetic materials, such as Celluloid, vulcanite, imitation pearl, stag, and horn and other plastics took the place of real bone, horn, ivory and pearl, some of the methods of treating scales by inlaying small designs with natural pearl and metal wires were most effective.

The two thin panel-shaped metal outlines shown at the top of Fig. 23 and the $\frac{1}{8}$ in. pearl units shown on either side of the pocket knife scales were forced into the black buffalo horn and tortoiseshell scales under slight, but warm, pressure after the scales had been previously shaped under much stress and high temperatures in steel dies. The thin pearl used for inlaying was known as 'snail shell' or 'green ear'. Some of the pieces were no thicker than cartridge paper and after pressing into the horn scale could be polished flush with it. No decorating has been effected in this or similar methods for at least fifty years.[1]

Another effective method of decorating pocket knife scales was by the stamping of designs in solid metal—either silver, nickel or aluminium. The process was much in demand for advertising purposes, many of the parts being made in France and Germany and then sent to Sheffield.

Decorative etching, gilding and oxidising in colours were being extensively practised in Sheffield at about the same time—the second

[1] These pocket knife specimens were collected by Mr. Frank B. Colver, managing director of George Wostenholm and Son, Ltd., Sheffield, who kindly presented them to me. Mr. Colver is one of the few people who can recall that this process of decoration was introduced to his firm in the mid-nineteenth century by a Frenchman named James Malangré, who settled in Sheffield and ultimately taught foreign languages.

half of the nineteenth century. It is probable that French, German and Scandinavian manufacturers were more expert in these processes than their Sheffield contemporaries. The northern countries, in particular, excelled in coloured oxidising and patination and their work was of a fairly permanent quality.

Because they were of such personal importance to their owners, from early times up to the twentieth century, hunting knives have been given the greatest possible care and attention so far as the applied arts were concerned (Fig. 63). A fine example of this was a hunting knife produced in Sheffield with a stag hunt depicted in brass detail inlaid by pressure on a black horn handle.

The handles of table knives with blades of shear, cast or stainless steel received more attention from the decorating cutler than did the blades, and some of the processes are described in Chapter 6.

With the exception of pen and pocket knives, no articles of cutlery in everyday use during the eighteenth and nineteenth centuries were subject to so much decorative detail as were razors, which were made in a great variety of shapes and sizes, types of points, backs and tangs, as is described in Chapter 9. The scales and handles were generally made by the same processes as the coverings of pocket knives. In addition to plain black or clear horn scales, there were bone, tortoiseshell, ivory, pearl and silver. Ivory and pearl were either plain or carved, while silver was engraved or chased. Horn and tortoiseshell scales were shaped in hot dies under pressure and pearl and metal inlays were often inserted while the scales were still warm.

An ivory razor scale decorated with a panel design of 276 silver pins firmly inlaid in holes $\frac{1}{32}$ in. deep is illustrated in Fig. 23. The drilled holes do not penetrate right through the ivory scale, even though examination under a magnifying glass reveals signs of their having been lightly tapped. Regularity in the spacing of the two sizes of wire suggests that a template was used in drilling. This example of point or 'piqure' work, as it was known, is not an exceptional instance of craftsmanship for its period—about 1840.

The other ivory razor scale illustrated in Fig. 23 has a natural design spray, incorporating the rose, shamrock and thistle modelled in relief in a hard brown enamel and picked out in gold detail, which shows no sign of tarnish. Queen Victoria's head executed in an ordinary black stain etching with the date of her Golden Jubilee—1887—is evidence of the year of

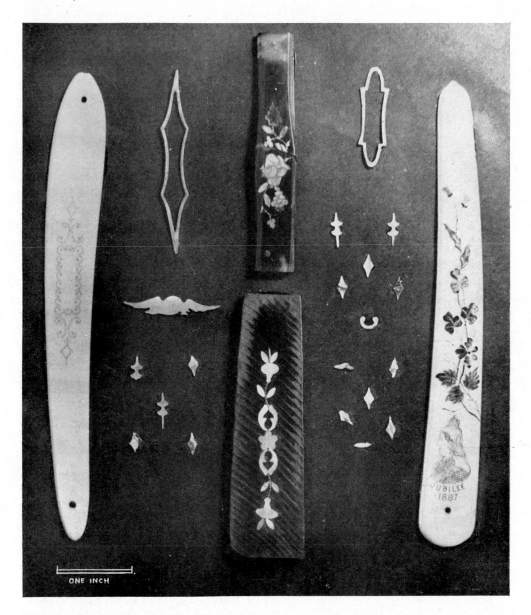

ONE INCH

Fig. 23. Specimens of the fine craftsmanship of cutlery decorators during the nineteenth century

The ivory razor scale on the left contains 276 inlaid silver pins (1840). The horn scales in the centre are inlaid with pearl. The ivory razor scale on the right has a design incorporating the rose, shamrock and thistle, modelled in relief in brown enamel and picked out in gold detail (1887). The other items are two metal wires and 18 pearl segments used for inlaying (1860).

89

manufacture. A slight brown discoloration on the back of the ivory suggests that it was stoved.

This technique has all the fine detailed workmanship demonstrated in French or Japanese art, but it is not possible to say how the floral design was effected.

The decoration of the backs and tangs of razors was a much-practised art long before emery or artificial grindstones superseded the natural fine-grained sandstones that were quarried from the blue bed of Brincliffe. Some eighteenth- and nineteenth-century grinders considered that 'jimping', as this practice was known, was an everyday job. It entailed the cutting of forty ribs side by side in the space of an inch across the back of a tang $\frac{7}{16}$ in. wide. The last man in Sheffield to do this on a natural grindstone cut the nicks in its surface with the edge of a piece of commercial tinplate, toughened by hammering. To-day this would be effected with a diamond point, such as might be used to prepare a wheel for cutting teeth in bread saws on an artificial grindstone.

A variety of patterns were produced by combinations of jimps—short and long flutes, bevels, nicks and facets that extended the length of the back of the tang. A jimped tang can be seen on the razor shown sixth from the top in Fig. 50.

In the nineteenth century it was quite a common custom to bronze razor blades before fitting them into scales. A number were fixed side by side on their backs on a flat tin plate and placed in a domestic oven until the heat gave them the colour of bronze. Incidentally, at the same time, this slightly reduced the hardness of the steel on what was known as 'army pattern' razors.

Another method of ornamenting razor tangs was by the chasing of a design with a hammer and punch.

Until the 1914–18 World War, ordinary long-style razors had been hollow ground by 'nicking in', or 'straight downing', on a sandstone that measured about 18 to 20 in. in diameter and which was either grooved or ribbed. The blade was held lengthwise and roughly ground from heel to point while being moved up and down the face of the stone, each side of the blade being ground alternately.

The shoulders had then to be cut in across the width of the blade, at the same time as the finer grinding process was being performed on a 6, 5, 4 or 3 in. diameter stone—the size varying according to the depth of hollow required.

The razor-grinding machine which could handle all rough grinding

Fig. 24. English seventeenth-century cutlery at Sheffield City Museum, reproduced by courtesy of the Museum

with two artificial stones running opposite each other, was invented early in the 1900's. These stones which varied in size, from 3 to 7 in. in diameter, according to depth of hollow, ground across the blade from back to edge and were controlled by a hand lever on the grinder's right side. The shoulders were cut simultaneous to the grinding of both sides of the blade. Afterwards, final fine grinding, by careful fingering, was necessary.

At the end of the nineteenth century, many of the details of design and variety of scissor patterns were lost with the change from production by hand to mechanical manufacture. Two-thirds of the fancy patterns illustrated in Figs. 56 and 58 were dependent on hand craftsmanship for their style and decoration. Even the rough forging and shaping was effected with a number of small removable tools that were fitted into the scissor-maker's anvil. The ornamental details were filed by hand and drilled, while the shanks and bows were finished off by hand burnishing with a curved steel burnish. Most of this finishing work was carried out by women.

With the development of mass production, patterns were reduced in number and simplified. Hand work was required to a lessening extent, for the engineer and the stamping machine did most of the heavy tasks.

Among the lost arts of Sheffield cutlers is the 'close plating' of steel cutlery, a process of plating knives and forks of ordinary steel with sheet silver by the application of block tin as a solder. Close plating was practised in early times, before, it is said, the fusion-plating of cutlery in 'Old Sheffield Plate' style.

Close plating was effected by tinning the surface of a steel blade or fork after it had been thoroughly cleaned by chemicals. Thin sheet silver was then 'sweated-on'—that is, fixed by pressure with the aid of a soldering iron, while the tin was in a molten state. Even the back edge of the blade and the prongs of a fork had narrow pieces of sheet silver applied in this way, giving a rust-resisting surface.

The silver surface was decorated by the use of small punches and matting tools. This ornamental work was delicate in appearance, suggesting frost on a bright surface. This process of plating was chiefly used on steel dessert knives and forks, because it resisted the corrosion that is caused by fruit juices.

After a while the silver wore off the edge of the blade, which then became slightly rough owing to the corrosion of the bare steel edge on exposure. This rough cutting edge had something of the keenness of the old-fashioned shear steel without, however, its stains and distasteful flavour. The last man in Sheffield to practise the art of close plating is

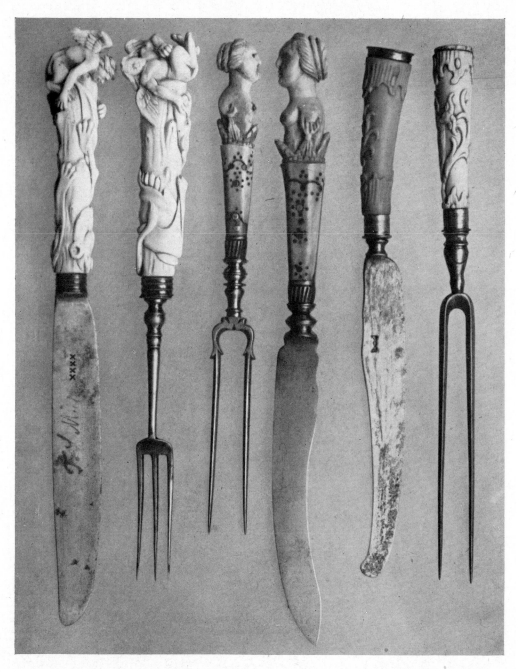

Fig. 25. German eighteenth-century table-ware with carved ivory handles, in the Sheffield City, Museum, reproduced by courtesy of the Museum

believed to have been named Smallwood. Over eighty years of age in about 1910, he went to his work in old-style dress, wearing a shiny top hat.

The saying 'By hammer and hand all things shall stand', might perhaps, be disputed by some to-day. Nevertheless, it enshrines a great basic principle. In the Sheffield light trades of the eighteenth and nineteenth centuries, forging by hand was an essential first process performed by men who had to stand all day lifting fairly heavy hammers.

The ash-wood handles depicted in Fig. 26 show the wear, in some specimens, of sixty years' continual use in light processes, such as small forgings, file-cutting underneath razor tangs, and the file-cutting on the backs of nail scissor blades and nail files that is seen in some of the best pocket knives. It can be noticed that a hammer used by a left-handed forger was so grooved by finger wear that it could not have been used by a right-handed worker.

Fig. 26. Hammers used in the nineteenth century for forging and small work on cutlery, showing the handwear caused by constant use over a number of years. The largest measures 11 in. long and the smallest, $6\frac{3}{4}$ in.

Specimens from the collections of the Sheffield Trades Historical Society and the author.

TABLE CUTLERY, BREAD KNIVES, BUTCHERS' AND HUNTING KNIVES, MATCHETS

CHAPTER 6

TABLE CUTLERY, BREAD KNIVES, BUTCHERS' AND HUNTING KNIVES, MATCHETS

THE steel knives and forks shown in Fig. 27 (top) were styles made in the eighteenth and nineteenth centuries and were generally of common quality carbon steel. This was, of course, before thick plastics (Celluloid) became available for the mass of users who could not afford ivory-handled knives and forks. Celluloid has much the same appearance as ivory and possesses qualities such as resiliency and ease of working not to be found in the more expensive material. Also about the end of the nineteenth century, solid nickel spoon-handled forks and spoons were introduced, almost at the same time as the development of the electro-deposition of silver, which gave low-priced articles all the appearance of expensive sterling silver.

The stag-handled knife and fork set, made with scale tang, pinned scale iron caps, illustrated in the top centre, was of a particularly common quality. The fork had no bolster, and in 1883 the wholesale price was 2s. 10d. per set of twelve knives and forks. Next in Fig. 27 are two knives of natural-shaped stag horn, with round resined-in tang and iron bullet caps. They are followed by a knife and fork, which are of scale tang with pressed black buffalo horn scales and three pins. These were made during the years 1820 to 1840. The remaining knives and the fork have round tangs with solid black horn handles.

On the left (top) of Fig. 27 are four cheap knives and forks in a variety of styles. There are forbucks, pressed checkered horn and inlaid horn handles, block tin run-on bolsters and solid bolsters.

Before the introduction of stainless steel, which had to be forged by machinery, the patterns in stainless steel illustrated in Fig. 27 (bottom) were generally hand-forged out of shear steel. A few were made of crucible cast steel by hand or machine.

The first five knives shown here are: octagon handle with straight blade and oval hollow bolster; candle end (oval) handle with straight blade and oval hollow bolster; candle end broad scimitar-swaged blade with oval hollow bolster; candle end handle with straight blade and egg waterloo bolster; candle end with narrow scimitar-swaged blade.

All these were machine-forged blades, hardened, tempered and then ground. They were given out to working cutlers along with Celluloid square slab handles, which they shaped by hand after the handles had been drilled and knocked on to the tangs. The bolsters and backs of the blades, still being black from hardening, were then rough-glazed or ground on an emery wheel, followed by fine glazing with emery and grease. Afterwards, the handles were polished on a cloth mop, or dolly, firstly with rottenstone and oil. This was followed by finishing-off with whitening mixed with water, a final gloss then being given on a dolly, with a little tallow as a lubricant.

The best-quality knives were hand burnished on the backs; mirror polishing of the blades was introduced about 1920. Up to this time, the maker's mark had been etched on stainless steel blades with acid, before the handle was put on, the blades then being mirror polished. Later, the knives were finished throughout before the manufacturer's mark was put on by a machine using electric needles that were controlled by a template.

The last five knives in Fig. 27 had rough-ground stainless steel blades on to which were brazed nickel silver alloy or other handles. The

---

Fig. 27. (Top). Knives and forks made in Sheffield of common quality carbon steel during the eighteenth and nineteenth centuries, before Celluloid became available for the mass of users who could not afford ivory-handled cutlery

From left to right:
Forbuck handle, with solid bolster.
Pressed checkered horn handle and scale tang.
Inlaid horn handle, with iron cap and solid bolster.
Pressed black horn handle, with iron cap and solid bolster.
Scale tang, stag handled knife and fork, with pinned scale and iron caps. Of cheap quality for the fork has no bolster.
Two natural shaped stag handled knives, with round tangs resined-in and iron bullet caps.
Knife and fork with pressed black buffalo horn scales, scale tang and three pins, dating from 1820–1840.

Fig. 27. (Bottom). Knives produced with stainless steel blades

From left to right:
Octagon handle, with straight blade and oval hollow bolster.
Candle end (oval) handle, with straight blade and oval hollow bolster.
Candle end handle, with broad scimitar-swaged blade and oval hollow bolster.
Candle end handle, with straight blade and egg waterloo bolster.
Candle end handle, with narrow scimitar-swaged blade.
The remaining five knives have stainless steel, rough ground blades and brazed-on handles of nickel silver alloy, silver plated or sterling silver.

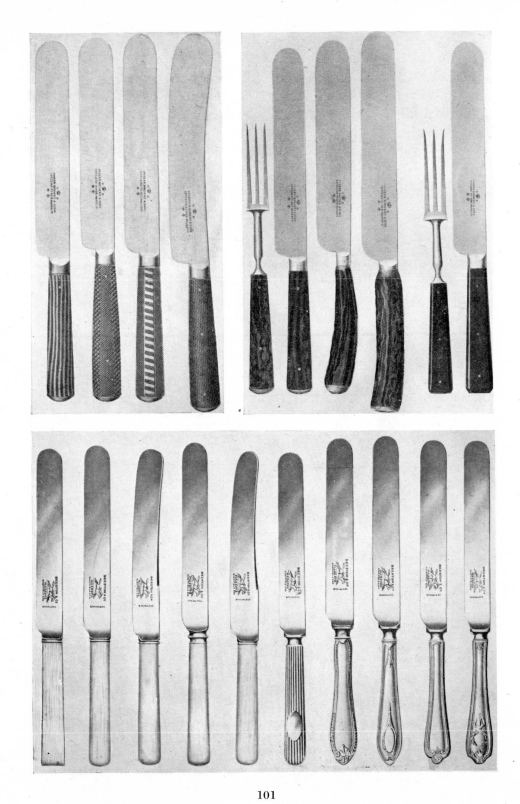

handles were stamped in two halves from steel dies, the halves being first brazed together and then on to the knife. They were next buffed in the same way as were spoons and forks, afterwards being silver plated by electro-deposition.

Following this, the handles were polished and the blades ground, polished, marked, whetted, wiped and wrapped for despatch.

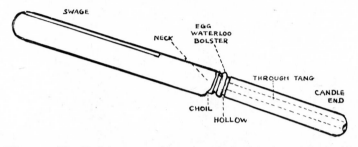

Fig. 28. Sheffield terms for a straight blade table knife

For many years after table knives had been made of stainless steel, carving knives continued to be produced with hand-forged shear steel—a practice that ceased about 1930.

A knife that became popular in the first half of the present century, ultimately being made in millions, was the serrated-edge bread knife. This bread saw was based on an ancient principle, dating back to Stone Age times, when small flint teeth were set in wooden framed sickles and harpoons. Comparatively modern Aboriginal knives from Australia also have small flints that are attached to a straight piece of wood by native resins and gums.

Serrated-edge sickles and grass-hooks were used by Belgian evacuee farm labourers who worked near Sheffield in about 1918. One of these labourers, who carried a small spike anvil and hammer at his belt, would put a serrated edge on his iron sickle by indenting the side of the edge.

Fig. 29. Sheffield knives of the nineteenth and twentieth centuries

(*Top*). From left to right:
Bone handle scale tang, with tommied shell or pinned-on bolster.
Block tin run-on bolster and rosewood scales.
Block tin run-on bolster and frame with ebony scales.
Four knives with block tin run-on bolsters.
Two table knives with vulcanite handles and hand-forged blades.
Three bread knives with carved boxwood handles.
(*Bottom*). Designs of the twentieth century made by the author, demonstrating the modern
    trend to escape ornate traditional styles.

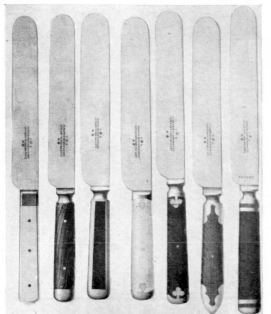
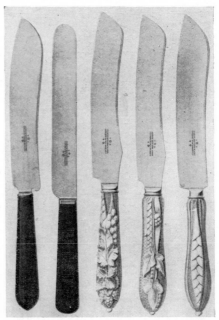
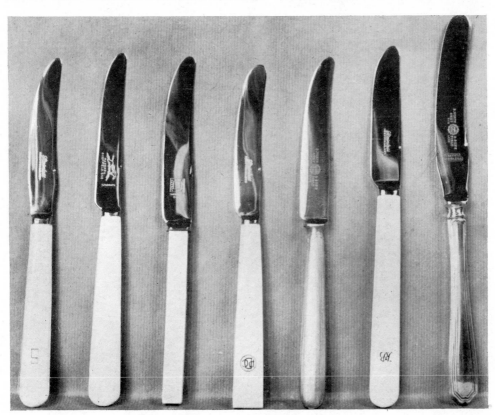

This type of anvil, known as a 'mower's anvil', dates from early Roman times.

In 1900, or perhaps earlier, a premier Sheffield firm of cutlers was producing a kitchen knife with saw teeth along the back to facilitate the cutting of bones when preparing meat. These teeth were similar to the serrations of a bread saw.

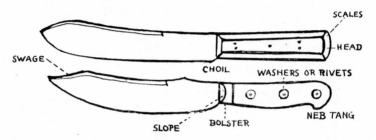

Fig. 30. Sheffield trade terms for a butcher's knife. (Top). Ordinary butcher's knife. (Bottom). Paraguay pattern

United States cutlers were the first to popularise a style in modern bread knives with a wavy cutting edge, which was later superseded in Britain by knives having definite saw teeth cut at an angle on the edge of

Fig. 31. Butchers', cooks' and camp knives

(*Top*). Left to right:
Butcher's knife, with ebony handle, brass bolster and screws.
Butcher's knife, with inlaid ebony brass framed handle.
Cook's knife, with rosewood handle.
Butcher's knife, with iron bolster and cap and rosewood handle.
Butcher's knife, with inlaid ebony brass framed handle.
Cook's knife, with iron bolster and rosewood handle.
Cook's knife, with metal bolster, three brass washers and rosewood handle.
Camp knife, with brass cap and bolster and an imitation stag handle.

(*Bottom*). Left to right:
Hunting, or dagger, knife, with chequered ebony handle and metal guard.
Butcher's knife, with rosewood handle.
Butcher's knife, with ebony handle and three brass washers.
Butcher's knife, with iron bolster and wedge-shaped redwood handle.
Butcher's knife, with redwood handle and three brass washers.
Butcher's knife, with redwood handle, three brass washers and clipt point.
Cook's knife—'Paraguay butcher'—with rosewood handle.
Cook's knife—'Paraguay butcher'—with metal bolster and rosewood handle.
Cook's knife, with rosewood handle and two brass screws.
Butcher's knife, with ebony handle and three brass screws. The blade is hand-forged shear steel.

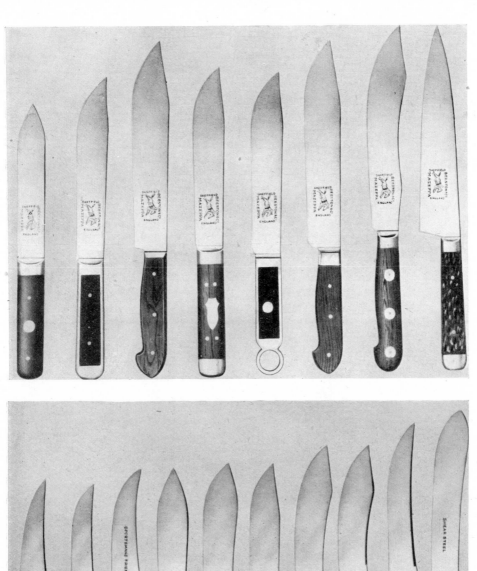

the blade. In some, the slope of the tooth was reversed every 2 in. There was little variation in the styles of the different manufacturers.

Housekeepers brought up in Victorian days were slow to accept the innovation of the bread saw, preferring a plain hand-forged shear steel knife without serrations.

It appears that England was the only country to make use of cases, boxes, and cabinets for cutlery during the nineteenth century. Until about 1850, it was the practice in Sheffield—the world centre for quantity production—to wrap all table cutlery, pocket knives and small tools in parcels of a dozen each. Those shipped abroad, as well as any sent in bulk supplies for the home market, were packed in barrels.

By the end of the nineteenth century, a wide variety of cases and boxes were in general use in Sheffield, for tea spoons, children's knife, fork and spoon sets, tea knives, fruit knives and forks, silver-plated fish eaters, fish carvers and later for stainless steel carver sets. There were also elaborate polished oak or mahogany cabinets for both home and export markets, containing sets of between sixty and 110 pieces of cutlery. Some of these cabinets were, in themselves, handsome pieces of furniture. (A more detailed description of methods of packaging and transporting cutlery is contained in Chapter 11.)

The Sheffield maker of fine table cutlery looked upon matchets as edge tools rather than cutlery, because of their weight, size and lack of fine

---

Fig. 32. Matchets, butchers' and trade knives

(*Top*). Left to right:
Matchet with green horn handle, straight neb.
Straight neb matchet, with green horn handle.
Two matchets with black horn handles, straight neb.
Green horn handle, with snake motif on blade, straight neb.
Green horn handle, straight neb.
Brass wire strapped beechwood handle, straight neb.
Pistol shaped neb made in wood and wrapped with brass wire.

(*Bottom*). Left to right:
Butcher's knife, with rosewood handle, five pins and no bolster.
Butcher's knife, with boxwood handle.
Shoemaker's knife, with turned whitewood handle.
Glazier's putty knife, with ebony handle and round tang.
Glazier's putty knife, with glass slots.
Glazier's putty knife, with ebony handle.
Glazier's hacking knife, with leather scales.
Glazier's putty knife.

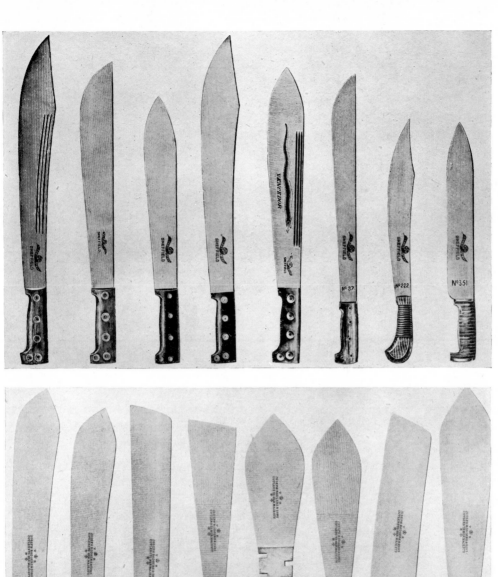

finish. Some of the heavier patterns were used abroad for clearing bush land, cutting tracks through forests, felling small trees, fighting at close quarters; in fact, as a rough all-purpose tool.

This was particularly the case in the jungle country of South America and the West Indies, where the purchasing power of the native was low and where he lived at close quarters with nature at its wildest. He had to be satisfied with one strong implement—quality of steel as understood in the more civilised countries of western Europe was unknown to him. The lowest price and quality, as long as it would harden and temper, was considered good enough for the native trade. However much the native might abuse the edge, he could readily put another on after a rough fashion.

Some of these matchets, however, were made in better qualities of steel, as were the last two sword knives illustrated in Fig. 33. Matchets shown in Fig. 32 were of a cheap variety, the handles generally being of green or black horn pressed by hand into shape in hot steel dies, one pair at a time.

While Sheffield-made matchets have played a vital role in controlling vegetation and cultivating crops in backward areas, natives have found them useful weapons in times of strife. They were used in South American revolutions and, more recently, by Mau Mau terrorists in Kenya, where they are known as 'pangas'. One Sheffield firm alone, that of S. and J. Kitchin and Sons Ltd., produces three-quarters of a million matchets, including those which have been used by the Kikuyu tribesmen. In 1953, they were sold to natives at about 3s. 6d. to 3s. 9d. each, the price being kept low because of strong German and Czechoslovakian competition. German competition has, in fact, grown so strong in many cutlery markets, that manufacturers of this type of knife have been considering ways of expanding sales on the British markets.

The Kitchin family appears to have settled in Sheffield about 1737, from north Nottinghamshire. A member of the family was then apprenticed to a cutler.

An idea of the great variety in patterns of Bowie, dagger, hunting, butcher's and Saladero knives may be gathered from the fact that in one book alone in my possession more than 600 styles are illustrated. Saladero knives were chiefly produced for South American markets.

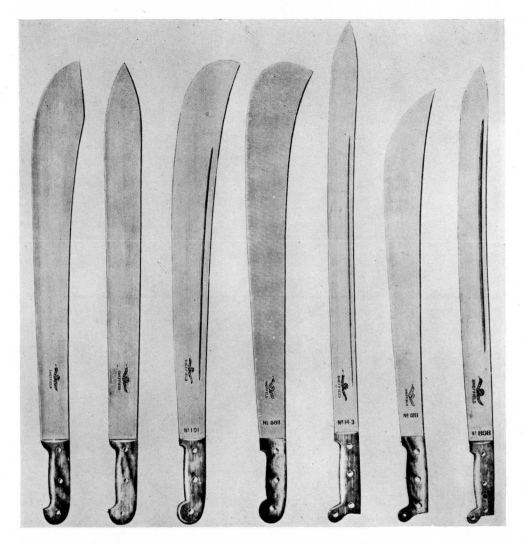

Fig. 33. Matchets and sword knives with green horn handles

Left to right:

Two with neb tang, two with round ends, three shaped neb that were of better quality steel than the others. As matchets were made principally for native markets they were produced in cheaper qualities to keep the price down. Sword knives were often 36 in. long.

SPOONS AND FORKS

CHAPTER 7

SPOONS AND FORKS

LITTLE use appears to have been made of spoons during prehistoric times, but the fact that spoons were in existence in those days—if only to a limited extent—has been established by the discovery of marrow scoops of Palæolithic origin and the clay spoons of the later Neolithic stage. There is no doubt that when man first began to cook and to boil water, which he effected in very early times by placing heated stones in the liquid, he used sea shells to convey small portions to the mouth.

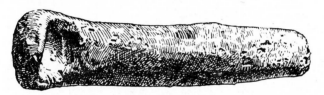

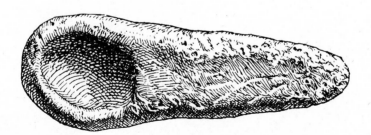

Fig. 34. Two Neolithic clay spoons from Hassocks, Sussex
(*Circa* 5000? B.C.) Sizes are 4 in. and 4½ in., respectively. (British Museum, *Stone Age Guide,* 1926, p. 111)

The ancient Egyptians used metal spoons of dainty form and proportions. These had a spike at the end of the handle, which was most likely intended to assist in extracting from their shells snails, a dish of which they were very fond, for they cultivated them in large quantities.

Bronze Age spoons are known to have been made both in Britain and on the Continent, but not many specimens have been discovered.

Associated with the period of the Roman invasion and occupation of Britain and found chiefly in Yorkshire is an unusual type of bone spoon that approximated in size to the present-day teaspoon. It was, however, made with a hole through the bowl, the purpose of which is not now apparent.

Silver spoons inscribed in Roman lettering and shaped much like those of the early Egyptians were found among the treasure unearthed at Milden-hall in Suffolk and in the Saxon Ship at Sutton Hoo. Dippers or skillets,

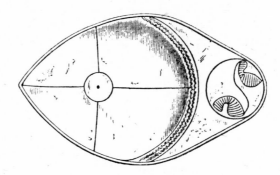

Fig. 35. Late Celtic bronze spoon from Crosby Ravensworth, Westmorland (British Museum, Iron Age Guide, 1925, p. 149)

which were larger than a spoon, are known to have existed prior to the year I B.C., while spoons with religious devices incorporated in their designs were possibly used for Druidical or other ceremonial occasions.

Spoons and ladles in brass or copper, for use in the kitchen and at the table, were introduced in Britain for the benefit of those who could not afford silver implements, and, as Anglo-Saxon feasting and wassailing gave way to more refined table manners, forks were made in the same metals—especially for those 'seated below the salt'.

Pewter was the first metal to be used in any quantity for the making of spoons. It was easily melted and the alloy of lead and block tin presented no difficulty either in mixing or casting. The low value and plentiful supply of lead, compared with silver, helped to increase the demand for pewter wares.

How early pewter was developed is not known, but it is fairly certain that up to the fourteenth century each person carried his iron or steel knife with him. The addition of a spoon and fork would have been something of an encumbrance. Pictures of fifteenth-century origin often show guests seated at the table holding a portion of food on the plate with their fingers and using a knife in the other hand. There is no sign of a spoon or fork.

The next material to be used extensively for the making of spoons was Britannia metal, which first appeared in Sheffield about 1769, when it was produced in large quantities by Hancock and Jessup, who not only cast small articles, such as spoons, but also rolled it into sheets, making it suitable for further manipulation into larger articles such as trays, dishes and so on. For spoons, the new metal was an improvement on pewter; being much harder, it took a good polish and in regular use was much whiter. It was, in fact, known to the trade as 'white metal' until 1797, since when it has been called Britannia metal, or, in its abbreviated form, 'B.M'.

During the seventeenth and eighteenth centuries and the early nineteenth century, low-priced steel and iron forks accompanied the spoon and knife for table use. Britannia metal was still too soft for fork prongs, although an attempt was made to produce them with a hard core of iron, copper or brass, covered with the softer metal. French and German makers were said to

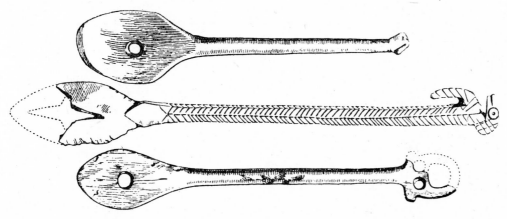

Fig. 36. Roman perforated bone 'spoons', from North Yorkshire caves

Sizes are 3½ in., 6 in. and 5 in., respectively. (British Museum, *Roman Britain Guide*, 1922, p. 49. First two spoons are omitted in revised edition. *Guide to the Antiquities of Roman Britain*, 1951, p. 39)

have accomplished this, but up to 1880 to 1885 forks produced in this manner never appeared in England in any great numbers. Although at that time, thousands of spoons of all sizes were being made in cast Britannia metal, the demand for B.M. spoons was rapidly declining, for nickel silver was coming into use.

The moulds for these spoons (Fig. 37) were produced in two halves, mostly in cast iron or brass. Each spoon was cast separately by a woman seated beside a cauldron of molten metal, into which she repeatedly dipped an iron ladle that was made to hold sufficient Britannia metal to produce one spoon.

Henry Holdsworth, in his factory, in Bramall Lane, Sheffield, not only made spoons in this metal, but also mustard pots and salt cellars, providing them with blue pottery linings. After the articles had been buffed and dollied, the final polish was given to the metal by the palm of the woman polisher, on which was spread a little oil.

In 1809, spoons like these were being sold by the manufacturer (or possibly by a factor or merchant) to ironmongers at 4s. 3d. per dozen. An invoice of that date from T. Carwood and Thomas, of Sheffield, to W. H. French and Son, Buckingham, included 'cutlery, flatware, files and small wares' and was endorsed 'per water from Derby to Birmingham, thence by Judd's boat'. On the same account were '2 set Black Tip London Octagon scale tang dub Tables at 11s. 6d.' Dessert knives and forks were described as 'portable slot'. The table cutlery was subject to a discount of 15 per cent., and table spoons to a discount of 20 per cent.

One other item on the account was '6 doz. Bufflo square Pockets 3s. 6d.', to which was added the note: 'Can't sell.' In December, 1806, the same firm had purchased goods from Sheffield cutlers or factors named Bishop, Potts, Carr, Parkin and Barber.

It was about this time that a new alloy, destined to play its part for at least 100 years in the Sheffield cutlery trade, appeared on the horizon. Harder than brass, it became known as 'German silver', or 'nickel silver', and was ultimately made in many degrees of quality. The various compositions of the new alloy ranged from 7 per cent. to 35 per cent. nickel, 50 per cent. to 65 per cent. copper, and 10 per cent. to 35 per cent. zinc, or spelter. When made with the higher nickel content, the metal did not readily stain or tarnish.

Something similar had been in use in China for hundreds of years and was spoken of by Westerners as 'white bronze' or 'paktong'. Edward Thomason experimented with this alloy in Birmingham about the year 1823, but he received little encouragement.

In 1830, a German named Guitike came to Sheffield from Berlin with a sample, but his metal was said to be too brittle for industrial use. By

Fig. 37. Spoon moulds and nickel silver spoons and forks

(_Top_). Spoon mould in brass for casting pewter rat-tail pattern spoons, with two spoons—that on the top showing the 'pour' remaining on the end of the bowl. English, _circa_ 1680. (_By courtesy, Sheffield City Museum._)

(_Bottom_). Silver plated on nickel silver spoons and forks. All these patterns are in hall-marked sterling silver and were made in Sheffield during the nineteenth century.

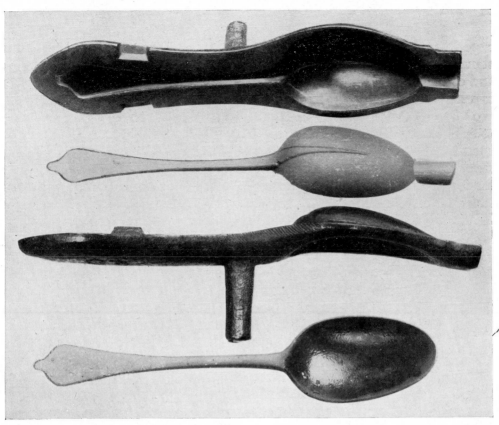

experiment and new arrangement of formula, however, it soon became the standard metal. It was cheap enough to supersede Britannia metal, brass and copper for spoons and forks, and to meet a demand for something less expensive than solid sterling silver. With a good plating of silver, it was used for hollow-ware.

The manufacturing trade still uses the words 'German silver', shortened to 'G.S.', when used as a base metal for hollow-ware, while 'nickel silver' is generally taken to be a description of a high nickel-content metal for forks and spoons. When, however, these articles are plated with pure silver by electro-deposition, they are said to be 'electro-plated on nickel silver', which is abbreviated to 'E.P.N.S.'

Britannia Metal and Spoons of the Poor

Britannia metal was invented in Sheffield, which appears to have been the only centre to handle it in any quantity from 1770 onwards. Pewter, which Britannia metal superseded, was a tin-lead alloy, and had been in use for a long period, a guild having been incorporated in London as early as 1482.

Pewter was chiefly worked in the form of castings, even for the manufacture of hollow-ware, but Britannia metal was more malleable. The general formula for B.M. was ninety-two parts block tin, six parts antimony (to stiffen the alloy) and one or two parts copper. Initially known as 'white metal'—until about 1797—it was much more hygienic than pewter. When it became more popular—about the end of the eighteenth century—the new alloy was referred to as 'Britannia metal'.

It could be cast into spoons, or rolled, spun and manipulated into hollow-ware much more easily than pewter.

Some of the earliest makers of B.M. spoons were Hancock, Jessop and Richardson. In 1825, Sheffield manufacturers of Britannia metal wares numbered twelve, and among them were James Dixon & Sons, Cornish Place, who in 1953 were still producing B.M. tea services in the same, although much enlarged, factory, as well as sterling silver and E.P.N.S. wares, together with articles in B.M. with a deposit of silver. These latter products are marked 'E.P.B.M.' to distinguish them from electro-plate on nickel silver goods (E.P.N.S.) and from sterling silver wares, which bear the Assay Office marks. This method of marking is followed by all British cutlery manufacturers to-day.

By 1845 there were fourteen Sheffield firms engaged in the production of B.M. goods, and many of their names had been added to the Sheffield directory since 1825. Some were also listed as being makers of 'German silver' goods with a silver deposition.

Fig. 38. Nineteenth-century Britannia metal tea and table spoons. All were made in Sheffield

Quoting from the account books for 1857–8 of a manufacturer of Britannia metal goods, chiefly teapots, Dr. J. E. Tyler, M.A., of Sheffield University, says[1] that spinners, makers-up of parts, and rubbers (hand polishers), might work a fifty-eight-hour week, and that the weekly wage, based on the average for twelve months, worked out at 26s. for the spinner, 23s. 6d. for the maker and 7s. for the rubber, who in all probability would be a married woman. Tyler assumes that the full hours per week were never worked. The maximum weekly wage for the spinner might rise to 33s., with the other workers earning wages in proportion.

Dessert, or pudding, spoons were not generally used during the eighteenth and nineteenth centuries, while forks were of steel and nearly always made with three prongs. Knives and forks were sold in sets—12 pairs forming a complete set. This was the practice on the Continent and in North and South America, as well as in Britain. People of humble station considered themselves fortunate if they had three eating tools—table knife, fork and spoon. They did not always possess a teaspoon and as late as 1920, the visitor to a café in a small French town would often be served with coffee in a basin, and a pewter table spoon with which to drink it.

The spoons illustrated in Fig. 38, are in two main sizes, the table spoons being all approximately $8\frac{1}{4}$ in. long and the teaspoons varying from 5 to $5\frac{1}{2}$ in. I do not recollect seeing in France, fiddle pattern spoons such as those shown in the second, third and fifth positions on the top row of this plate, rather it was the custom to use there the old English table or tea-spoons, like the tea or ridge pattern that is shown first and fourth on the top row.

Departure from the normal pattern of B.M. spoon is seen in the fifth, sixth and seventh specimens (top row), for they were made with a rib running down the back of the shanks to strengthen them. The fourth has what might be called Queen Anne flutes on the back of the bowl. The first and third are of extremely soft metal, probably with a higher content of lead than normal, and bear a nearer imitation to a hall-mark than any of the others. The table spoons were made with a substantial amount of B.M. being quite $\frac{3}{8}$ in. thick in the shank. All the spoons on the plate appear to have been made by casting, circa 1825.

John Heathcote, who made all the table spoons shown, lived at Pye Bank, Sheffield, in 1825, but his name was not included in the Sheffield list of makers for that year. The marks 'Cowlishaw' on the fourth teaspoon and 'Cowlishaw Sheffield' on the second and ninth teaspoons denote a name that appeared in the 1837 Sheffield directory as a buffer.

The fifth, sixth and seventh teaspoons, each with a raised rib on the

[1] *Transactions of the Hunter Archæological Society* (Sheffield, 1938).

back of the shank, appear to be marked 'W. Locke, Sheffield', while the third and eighth are marked 'Z. Sarson'. The first in the top row and the three teaspoons in the lower row are all marked 'Holdsworth'.

The name of William Holdsworth figured in the Sheffield Directory of 1825, being described as a 'Britannia spoon manufacturer, grocer and rag merchant'. The four Holdsworth spoons illustrated, in addition to the maker's name, are also marked with a crown and the motto 'V.R.' (Victoria Regina). They could not, therefore, have been made before 1837, the year that Queen Victoria came to the throne. As a young lad in 1884, I saw many gross of these spoons being cast and prepared in Bramall Lane, Sheffield, by a woman caster for Henry Holdsworth, a descendant of William Holdsworth.

I can also recall—as no doubt can many others of my generation—the use of pewter spoons in England as late as 1890. Until about 1850, spoons of lead and pewter were used in country districts in the Isle of Man. It is recorded[1] that at this time feasts that were held in the homes of the island's fishermen, always started with broth served in wooden piggins. Although horn spoons were made in the villages, the broth was drunk with a shell similar to, but longer than, a mussel.

It was the custom of the old women who travelled round the parishes to carry their own moulds and crucibles, called 'cressets', in which spoons about 7 in. long, the size of the modern dessert spoon, were cast, or 'run'. They were cast at the price of $\frac{1}{2}d$. each. The inside of the mould was smoked with the wick of a tallow candle to prevent the metal sticking, one treatment sufficing for six spoons.

Before resin was first developed as a flux, tallow was useful in assisting the flow of metal, and spoon and other moulds had to be kept as warm as possible.

[1] *Manx Antiquities*, by Kermode and Herdman (University Press of Liverpool, 1914).

PEN AND POCKET KNIVES

CHAPTER 8

PEN AND POCKET KNIVES

POCKET knives were used as long ago as the first century A.D., as evidenced by the collections of Roman pocket (clasp or shut) knives in St. Mary's Museum, York, and Cirencester Museum (Fig. 39). One of these, discovered at South Shields, is of ivory and a portion of its blade is still intact. A figure of a gladiator carved on the handle has a shield on his left arm and a short sword in his right hand. His left leg is greaved and there is a bronze ring where the handle joins the blade.

Another, also with ivory scales, has a $3\frac{7}{8}$-in. blade and it was found at Cilurnum, on Hadrian's Wall, with other Roman remains. A dot-and-circle decoration that is incised on the ivory is often to be seen on Roman, Danish and medieval bone and ivory objects. Other Roman pocket knives in this collection are of bone or ivory.

Some of the handles of Roman knives to be seen in the York Philosophical Society's Museum were dyed green, a practice that continued until the nineteenth century, so far as ivory is concerned.

In a lecture that he gave in 1883, R. E. Leader, the well-known Sheffield historian, quoted Juvenal as having said in the first century: 'I do not possess an ounce of ivory. . . . Nay, my very knife handles are of bone, but they never make my victuals taste nasty, nor does the fowl cut up any the worse on this account.'

R. E. Leader was of the opinion that the pen knife, as distinct from the pocket knife, was first produced early in the eighteenth century; certainly it could not have been much earlier. To shape a pen out of a quill was a delicate operation not easily performed with a pocket knife blade. Apart from the shaping of quills, the pen knife found a useful place in the needle-work basket for unpicking stitches and so on.

In making pen knives and the smaller pocket knives, Sheffield craftsmen were capable of a degree of fineness and adjustment in handling that has been equalled only in the production of jewellery (Figs. 40 and 42). The blades of a well-made knife of this class should, when opened out, lie straight in a line with the scales, but when shut each blade must pass and finally rest side by side, without wedging—no mean accomplishment.

The blades of a pen or pocket knife must also work, or 'walk', easily when either opening or shutting, and they should not shake from side to side. In the hand-forging of pen knife blades, some of which measure no more than 1 in. in overall length, the working cutler has to pay attention to the exact shape, the total length, the making of a nail nick and sometimes the making of a step in the tang, while the size of tang must be kept proportionate to the size of the cutting part of the blade.

All these points call for great skill, with delicate and well-directed blows from the hammer, and at the same time they must be accompanied by a fine adjustment of heating to a correct temperature of the rod, or 'string', of steel, which is being 'mooded' on the 'stiddy', or anvil.

A stiddy is a most complex tool, and it is made in a number of patterns to suit the different articles to be produced. The stiddy required for the forging of a pen knife blade has various faces and attachment of agons, or agirons, with which the hand forger nicks in the recesses, slopes the blade from back to edge, makes the choil and, finally, cuts off the blade from the rod. All this has to be accomplished before the steel becomes too cool, otherwise the structure of the steel might be crushed, or strained microscopically, and either crack in later processes or fail to give satisfaction in use.

The next step is to obtain the right heat before hardening, a process that is carried out by heating the blade cherry red and then quenching it in water or oil. Equal care is demanded in tempering to reduce the brittleness and obtain thereby the correct quality, which should take and maintain a good cutting edge after grinding and whetting. Neither hardening nor tempering

---

Fig. 39. Ancient Roman pocket (clasp or shut) knives found in England

(*Top*). 1. Ivory handle, about 3 in. long; blade missing. In York Philosophical Society's Museum.
2, 3. Bone handles, about 3 in. long; blades missing. Both are in York Philosophical Society's Museum.
4. Ivory handle, with a portion of the blade, from South Shields. The gladiator has a shield on his left arm and a short sword in his right on top of the shield. His left leg is greaved. There is a bronze ring where the handle joins the blade.
5. Ivory handle about $3\frac{7}{8}$-in. long from Cilurnum, on Hadrian's Wall. The dot-and-circle decoration incised on the ivory is well known on Roman, Danish and Medieval bone and ivory objects.

(*Bottom*). Roman pocket knives discovered at Corinium (Cirencester) and now in Cirencester Museum. 1, 2, cast bronze with greyhound and hare. 3, 4, 5, bone handles with bronze ferrules.

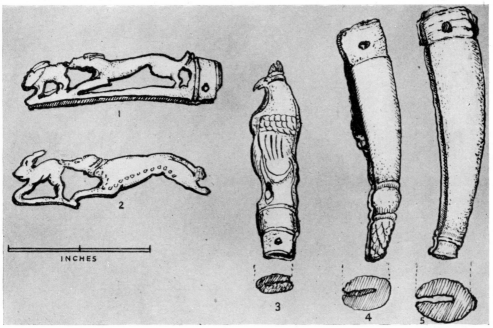

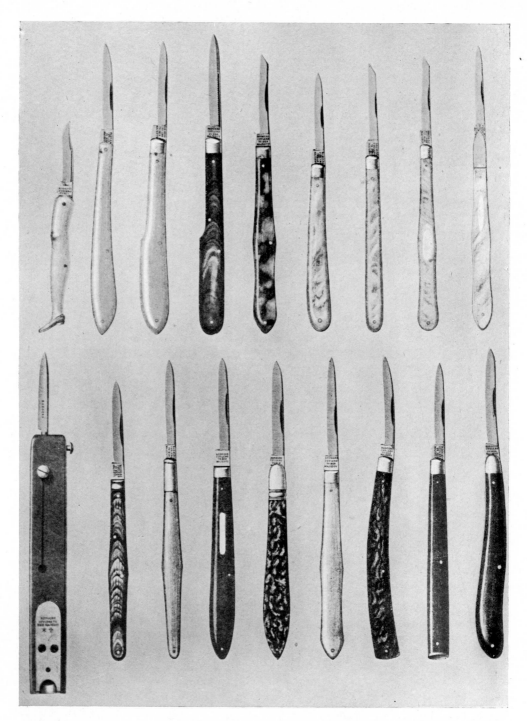

Fig. 40. Sheffield-made pen knives of the eighteenth and nineteenth centuries

The rectangular-handled knife, known as a 'pen machine' had a blade at one end that was used for the partial shaping of a quill.

are simple processes; they call for an accurate judgment that is acquired only after years of experience.

To those familiar with handicraft processes in general and the skilled methods required to produce cutlery in particular, the term 'art' will readily be granted for that extra quality that has been attained by Sheffield's pen knife cutlers. Their craft calls for something more than skilful practice or production to type.

One of the most interesting tools that is used in the production of pen or pocket knives is the parsa, or parser. The single parsa, an ordinary drill

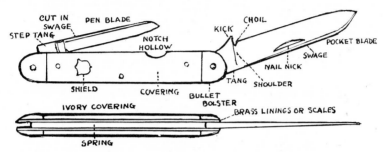

Fig. 41. Sheffield trade terms for pocket knife parts
Linings without bolsters are webs. Coverings are then called scales.

that is rotated by a fiddle bow, is used for boring a small, round hole, a method of drilling that has endured for thousands of years. By using a double parsa, however, the cutler can fashion any shape of hole or recess, including round, square, oval, oblong or heraldic. Examples of such shapes are shown on the knives illustrated in Figs. 40, 42, 44 and 45.

The double parsa, a hand-made tool, is controlled automatically by a fiddle bow, its double, or bifurcate, drill rotating in a steel template. As the drill rotates, the two legs follow the outline of the hole in the template and by their eccentric movement cut out the required shape. The depth of the hole is regulated by the shoulders of the cutters working on the template.

To make his double parsa, the cutler welds two pieces of thin steel rod at one end to form the point of the spindle, or drill, which rests in the breast-plate. Next, the two free ends are forged down thinly and finally shaped with a file to form the cutters. They are then hardened and tempered, followed by whetting on an oilstone. The driving of an ash-wood bobbin on to the spindle end completes the tool (Fig. 43).

The steel template is approximately $1\frac{1}{16}$ in. wide, and is pierced with any shape of opening, either square, round, oblong, oval, or heraldic. Tempering ensures that it will maintain its shape during constant use.

I

The template is held against the material to be recessed or pierced, the two cutting legs of the rotating parsa following its outline.

The shield, made either of gold, silver or brass, is then let into the recess, and to make it thoroughly secure the cutler usually pins through the shield to the material underneath. The surface is filed flush, and after the assembly of all the knife parts and pinning together, with a metal web between the blades and outer scales, comes the final polishing.

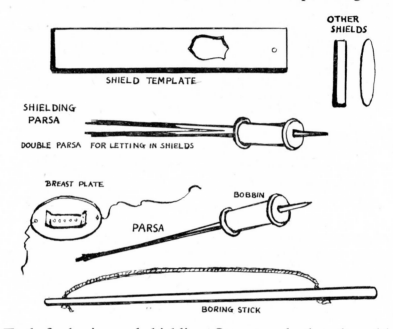

Fig. 43. Tools for boring and shielding. Square and other shaped holes can be drilled with the double parsa

No other process seems to be so practicable for the recessing, or boring, of pearl, ivory, tortoiseshell, Celluloid or silver; the only alternative being to engrave each recess laboriously by hand.

During the last 200 years, the double parsa must have had its most extensive use at the hands of the working cutler in the pen and pocket

---

Fig. 42. Sheffield pen knives of the eighteenth and nineteenth centuries

Each of these specimens differs in some detail. There are round, straight and hollow backs, for instance, while scales are made from silver, ivory, pearl, grey and black horn, stag horn, ebony and tortoiseshell. Those at the top of the illustration are mostly double-blade pen knives and those at the bottom are double-ended pen knives, that is they have a blade at each end.

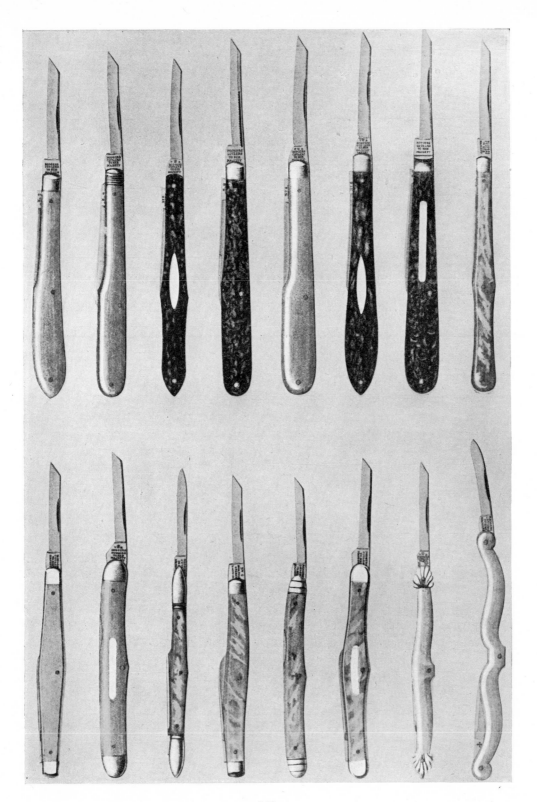

knife trade, for millions of better-class knives have been produced during that time with inlaid shields of varying shapes.

It is not possible to illustrate or enumerate within the pages of this book the vast variety of pen and pocket knife designs of past times, but some idea may be gleaned from catalogues of manufacturing or merchanting companies. Most of the pocket knives that are shown in Figs. 44 and 45, for instance, were included in lists issued by Sheffield manufacturers in the nineteenth century. The United States, as well as German cutlers, were making almost as great a variety at that time, and a catalogue of general hardware that was published by a U.S. merchant in 1893 contained 1,452 pages, each measuring $12\frac{1}{2}$ in. by 9 in. It weighed 15 lb. and was 4 in. thick. This firm claimed to stock 1,500 types of pocket knife, including American patterns as well as those of English and German cutlers. The hardware and cutlery catalogue of another merchant in the same territory weighed 21 lb.

Among a number of advertisements contained in the Sheffield Directory of 1845 is the claim of one firm of local cutlery manufacturers— not the largest by any means—to have in stock 20,000 to 30,000 dozens of 'general cutlery'; while another claimed stocks of '8,000 to 10,000 dozens of razors'. Altogether, some 1,000 local manufacturers of cutlery were listed in this directory.

Pen and pocket knives produced in Sheffield during the nineteenth century were equipped with numerous tools and implements, including button-hooks, corkscrews, stone-hooks, leather-borers, tweezers, nail-files, gimlets, saws, prickers, fleams, castrating blades, erasers, scissors, budding and grafting knives, cartridge extractors, screwdrivers, cigar-forks, shackles and tin-openers. A number of these are illustrated in Figs. 45 and 46.

Two-, three- and four-blade pen knives are shown in Figs. 42 and 44 in many shapes and materials, including pearl or silver and diamond cut or cross-hatched. Finely made, proportionate and well-finished, the pen knives shown in Figs. 40 and 42 are approximately $2\frac{1}{4}$ in. long and measure 4 in. overall. Many of them are not more than $\frac{1}{8}$ in. thick, including the two inner metal scales, spring and pearl scales. The usual width of this type of knife was, however, $\frac{1}{4}$ in. The blades, beautifully shaped, ground thin and flexible in use, were often only $\frac{1}{8}$ in. wide, including the swage on the back.

Each of the numerous patterns of pen and pocket knives differed in some detail. They were either round, straight or hollow-backed; with hollow, spear or slope points; and were made with either single or double blades. Materials for the scales were silver, ivory, pearl, grey and black horn, stag horn, tortoiseshell and ebony. Bone was occasionally used, but only for low-quality knives. Some pen knives were made with short bolsters, while a number of styles had no bolster at all.

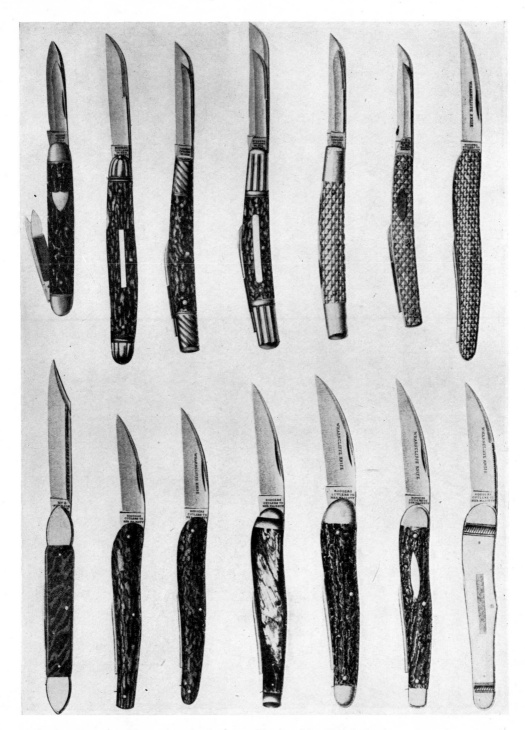

Fig. 44. Pen and pocket knives made in Sheffield during the nineteenth century

Beak-shaped blades and scales were known to the trade as 'Wharncliffe' pattern, and some had this name stamped on the blade. This style of knife, which, because of its large blade, is more aptly described as a pocket than a pen knife, is attributed to Earl Wharncliffe (sixteenth century). Most of the knives shown in Fig. 44 are 'Wharncliffe' pattern.

Other unusual types of pen or pocket knives that were made in the

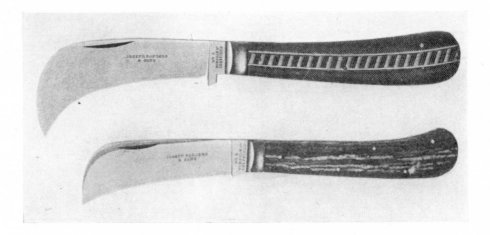

Fig. 45. Coffee pruner and a pruning knife

Fig. 46. Special purpose pen and pocket knives that were made in Sheffield

(*Top*). Left to right:
Pocket knife blade with button-hook, corkscrew, stone-hook, pen blade, leather borer and a picker and tweezer that are not shown. Stag scales.
Similar to the first, but with double hollow back, Wharncliffe shaped blade and turn screw end.
Ivory scales, with nail-file and cleaner.
Eight attachments, including two blades, saw, gimlet and pricker.
Six attachments, including fleam and picker and tweezer in the closed position.
Castrating blade and fleam in grey buffalo horn scales.

(*Bottom*). Left to right:
Three fleams in grey buffalo horn scales.
Three fleams in metal scales.
Desk knife with spigot-shaped ebony handle.
Heart-shaped eraser with smoothing end handle.
Combined pen and eraser blade.
Desk knife with metal cap.
Desk knife with round ivory handle.
Desk knife with stag tine handle.
Desk knife with rosewood or partridge wood handle.

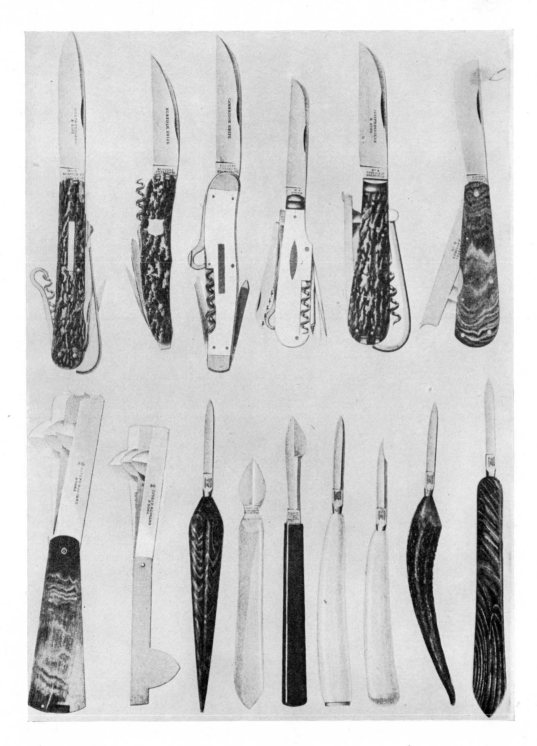

nineteenth century included a combined pistol and dagger, patented by 'Unwin and Rodgers' (a name that was mentioned in the Sheffield Directory of 1828); pocket folding fleams for bleeding, the obsolete surgical practice of opening veins; ladies' ivory pen knives with glove hook, measuring 2 in. when opened. A 'pen machine' that had a knife blade at one end to shape partially the quill, was fitted at the other end with a pressure cutter for shaping the pen and slitting the point. This tool was introduced late in the history of the quill pen, at a time when steel pens were coming into favour (Fig. 40).

Pocket knives were also made for gardening or trade purposes, and among special types were pruning, budding and grafting knives, coffee pruners, timber scribers and plumbers' knives.

Fig. 47. Pocket and other knives for trade use

(*Top*). Left to right:
Double-blade pocket knife with long nail nick and hollow back.
Double-blade pocket knife with small nail nick, round back and spear point.
Pocket blade with fleam and castrating blade.
Metal-scaled spike knife with one blade and shackle.
Metal-scaled knife with two blades and ring opener.
Metal-scaled knife with pressure spring to open blade.
Ivory-scaled knife with hole and blade for cigar-cutting.
Pocket pallet knife.
Pocket knife with extra thick blade and Gothic end scale.
Pocket knife with ivory tulip-shaped scales.

(*Bottom*). Left to right:
Double-blade 'palf' pocket knife.
Pocket knife with hollow back and blade known as a sheep foot shaper.
Pocket knife with spear-point blade and straight back.
Hollow backed double-blade pocket knife with corkscrew attachment.
Round backed double-blade pocket knife with corkscrew attachment.
Double-ended pocket knife with two spear blades and bullet bolsters.
Double-blade pocket knife with ivory scales.
'Clock' pattern double-blade pocket knife.

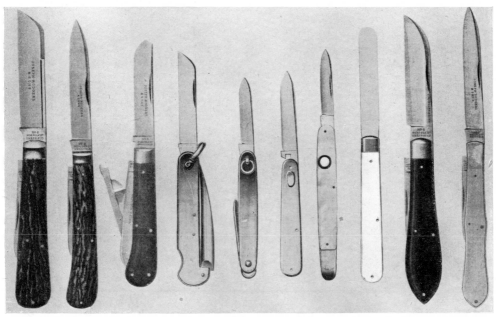

RAZORS

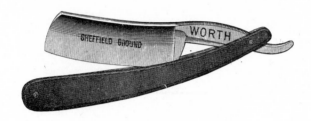

CHAPTER 9

RAZORS

FAST disappearing nowadays, the old style of razor that is known colloquially as the 'cut-throat' was made in numerous styles and shapes. It might, for instance, have a square, round, Irish, half-round, dish, hollow or half-hollow point, with either single or double shoulders, and it was produced in a variety of widths ranging from $\frac{3}{8}$ in. to 1 in.

The hollow-grinding of a razor was a highly skilled craft, with some razors being hollowed on a grindstone measuring no more than 2 in. in diameter. Flat or plain, half-hollow, extra-hollow or full hollow ground

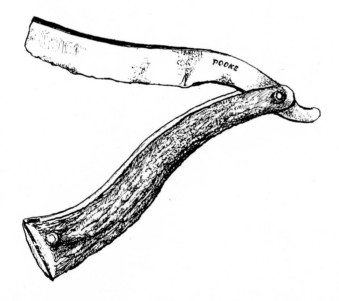

Fig. 48. Razor—of the eighteenth century (?). Thickness of the well-rounded, or 'quilled', back is $\frac{1}{8}$ in. Tine is of stag, natural shape and tang has been drawn down to $\frac{1}{16}$ in. thick. Pins are of brass with iron washers, while the head end is of iron

razors, could be made with flat, round or quill backs, with a grob on the point, and be jimped or file-cut on the back and fore side.

Marks were made either by striking-in with a punch, etching, electro-gilt, white frosted etching or gilt side marks after deep etching. The modern method is by an electrical etching machine that is fitted with a number of needles. If made without a mark, the open razor was known as 'blind'.

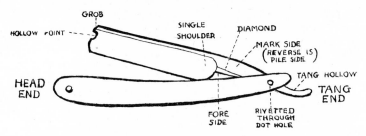

Fig. 49. Sheffield trade terms for razor parts

When made with a flat tang, it would have a 'diamond' bevel, but all tangs, even those of ivory, would have a dot-hole. The 'cut-throat' might have a monkey tang, thumb-hole or figure-three tang, any of which could be lapped, glazed or polished.

Materials used for the scales of nineteenth-century Sheffield-made razors were: black buffalo, either plain or inlaid with pearl; clear horn; grey buffalo; bone; ebony; ivory, either plain or fluted; xylo, either plain or pressed; pearl, either plain or fluted; vulcanite, plain or fancy; genuine or imitation 'spotted' tortoiseshell; aluminium.

Terms that are well-known in the Sheffield razor trade were quoted in *The Stone-floored Workshop*, a description of a Sheffield grinding 'hull', or workshop, that was written in blank verse by Edward Carpenter, the author of *Towards Democracy*. Carpenter referred to horsings, drums, slapping

---

Fig. 50. Razors, ancient and modern

1. Stone from Egypt.
2. Bronze from Ireland.
3, 4 and 5. Bronze Age.
6. Nineteenth-century razor in steel, from Japan.
7 and 8. Nineteenth-century, from China.
9. Nineteenth-century, from Siam.
10. Nineteenth-century, from Hindustan.
11 and 12. Bronze, from the Caucasus.
13. Nineteenth-century styles, from Sheffield.
14. Razor, from Turkey.
15 and 16. Nineteenth-century, from Persia.
17. Nineteenth-century monk razor, from the United States.

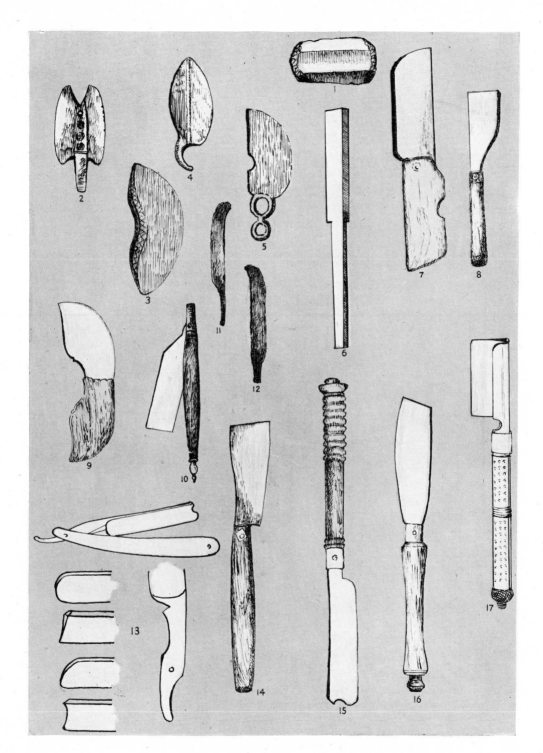

belts, trows (troughs), emery wheels, polishers, glazers, the men's talk of fancy backs, rattlers, sours, wasters, tangs, heels, shoulders and the fans that were used to expel the dust caused by grinding.

During recent years, the wafer-blade razor, which is known locally among Sheffield manufacturers and work-people as a 'pig scraper', has been claimed by the trade in the United States as being an American invention, because American skill in marketing, resulting in exceptionally large sales, successfully established this new type of shaving. It was, in fact, stated, as recently as January, 1952, in a British trade report of an exhibition held in the Science Museum, London,[1] that the safety razor was devised in 1847 by William S. Henson, a Londoner. It was also said that the wafer-blade was invented by King C. Gillette in 1895, who started producing it in 1901.

Fig. 51. One of the earliest wafer-blade razors

The Sheffield wafer-blade, however, was first produced some seventy years before the Gillette pattern. The earliest known reference to a wafer-blade, which had a guard along one edge, appeared in an advertisement in the Sheffield Directory of 1828. The text of this is reproduced below:

> New frame-bladed razor, which will be warranted and kept in order 12 months; it was first suggested by the celebrated David Hartley, Esq., M.P. for Hull and was made by Mr. Champion and his partner 14 years' ago (1814).

[1] *Razors Past and Present*, Science Museum, December 12, 1951, to January 9, 1952.

Fig. 52. Nineteenth-century hand-forged razors, made in Sheffield

Top to bottom:
Flat black scales, $\frac{5}{8}$-in., thumb-hole and half round point.
Ivory scales with thumb-hole, Irish point, hollow ground.
Ivory scales and tang with $\frac{5}{8}$-in. round point, hollow ground.
Ivory scales, $\frac{3}{4}$-in. round point, hollow ground and swaged back.
Cast aluminium imported scales, round chased tang and $\frac{5}{8}$-in. square point, hollow ground.
Ivory scales with jimped edge of tang, $\frac{3}{4}$-in. wide blade and Irish point.
Black buffalo scales with $\frac{3}{4}$-in. wide blade, long cut quill back and hollow point.
Black buffalo London head scales, with $\frac{3}{4}$-in. wide blade, round point.
Black buffalo scales with $\frac{3}{4}$-in. wide blade, slope heel and point.
Black buffalo horn scales, with $\frac{3}{4}$-in. wide blade and plain polished side, round point.
Ivory scales with $\frac{3}{4}$-in. wide blade and plain (flat) ground, dish point.

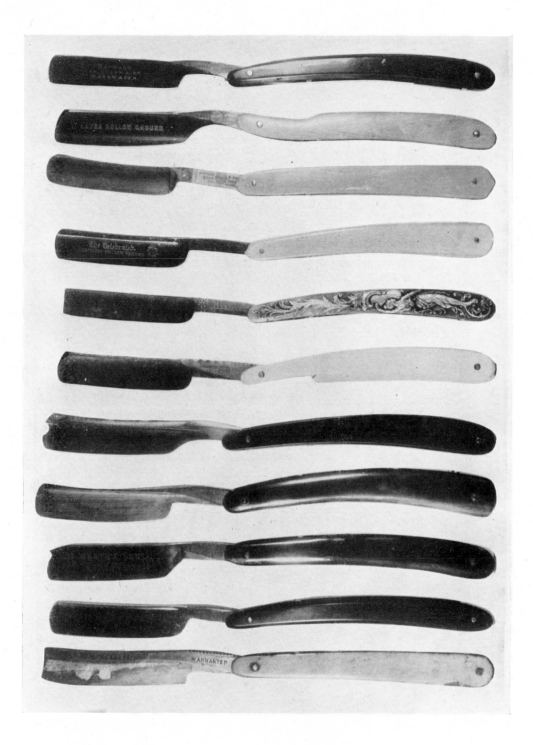

S. Parkes, Esq., F.L.S. has made the following remarks on this razor in the 4th volume of his *Chemical Essays* (page 486):

'When instruments have a thick back and a fine edge, it is almost impossible ever to give them a uniform temper by the old method for there will always be danger of the edge being lowered too much before the other parts become regularly heated throughout. This difficulty occurs particularly in razors, where the thickness of the back is always a formidable obstacle to the attainment of a uniform regularity of hardness.

'The inconvenience of this particular instrument has been so great that Messrs Rhodes and Champion, of Sheffield, have manufactured what they call the "New Frame Bladed Razor" in which the back and the finger-hold are made of an admirable alloy of copper not subject to rust, and the blade only is made of steel. These blades being nearly as thin at the back as the edge, can be tempered without incurring the danger already mentioned, and when let into a copper back, it becomes a complete instrument.'

The manufacturers also stated:

The inequality of thickness that necessarily prevails in razors manufactured in the usual way, has ever been found a formidable obstacle to the attainment of an uniform regularity of hardness, without which no good razor can possibly be made.

The principle on which the new frame-bladed razor is manufactured, is calculated to obviate this great defect; and it is easily discernible that by no other means can this essential and indispensable quality, with equal certainty, be produced. The heel, or finger-hold part of the blade, being composed of a metal not subject to rust is another important recommendation. A confidence may, therefore, be reasonably entertained, that a single trial will not fail to establish the decided superiority of the new frame-bladed razor over every other. It shaves extremely close and will be found both smooth and pleasant in use.

(N.B. A strop, occasionally used, will keep this razor in excellent condition for years, as it will very rarely, if ever require the hone.)

Fig. 53. Nineteenth-century hand-forged razors, made in Sheffield

Top to bottom:

Left, $1\frac{1}{4}$-in. blade, for cutting velvet. This is shown 'in the rough'—that is, before finishing and polishing.

$\frac{3}{8}$-in. blade with double shoulder and nostril shaver, made for the United States.

Small size $\frac{5}{8}$-in. wide blade with ivory scales.

Early type hollow ground razor, made specially for the Irish trade.

Monkey tang 'Mab' style razor—'Mab' being a maker's brand.

Corn razor with imitation tortoiseshell scales and square point.

Cast aluminium scales with round chased tang, $\frac{5}{8}$-in. hollow point, hollow ground. Scales were imported either from France or Germany and fitted to a Sheffield blade.

Black vulcanite scales, round point and long cut—that is with no shoulder.

Clear horn scales, small end undressed, with slope point thumb hole. Wholesale price for export in 1883 was 10*s.* per dozen.

Imitation tortoiseshell scales with $\frac{5}{8}$-in. plain polished, side etched, blade. Of good quality, the wholesale price for export in 1883 was 10*s.* per dozen.

Round black scales, $\frac{3}{4}$-in. fancy swaged back and Turkish point.

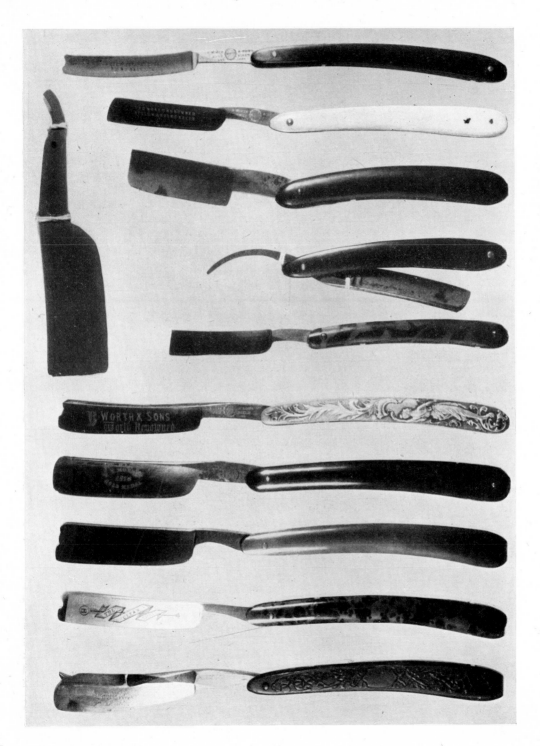

Thus, the wafer razor blade fitted into a frame came into existence.

A stock of 8,000 to 10,000 dozens of razors that was held by a Sheffield firm in 1845, included a number of these frame-backed razors.

It was common knowledge in Sheffield that one of the largest cutlery firms at one time during the nineteenth century held orders for razors for India which would take 'seven years to complete'. These were of a plain type known as 'monkeys' in the trade, but made of good quality steel.

At that time, production was dependent on hand craftsmanship, and such delayed deliveries, with other considerations, induced the development of mechanical processes. It was not, however, until 1910 to 1915 that the heaviest process in the grinding of razors was undertaken by machines.

'Statements'—that is, rates of pay for the many processes in the manufacture of razors—were drawn up and agreed to by both manufacturers and workmen long before this: as early as 1810. In 1814, during a bad period of trade, manufacturers demanded that fourteen blades should be reckoned at the price of twelve—'fourteen to the dozen'—to which the men had to submit. This arrangement continued for 100 years, and shortly after the start of the First World War the demand for razors was great and grinders, who were at a premium, were able to insist on 'twelves' again.

The grinding machines that were introduced at about the same time enabled the rough hollowing of razors to be effected on both sides of the blade at the same time, instead of the former practice of 'nicking-in' one side of the blade on a corrugated stone. The shoulders, also, were cut in by the two opposite stones of a machine in one operation, whereas shouldering had entailed another extra process when grinding by hand. Even with the use of machines, it was still essential that the fine grinding of the edge of the blade should be done by skilled craftsmen before glazing, buffing and polishing the blade.

Although at the beginning of the First World War, the British Government was placing huge orders for the best type of full hollow ground razors, chiefly for the Royal Navy, the Gillette style of safety razor was already sweeping the world's markets. The safety razor, with its blades that lasted only a day or so, became increasingly popular, in spite of the fact that the 'cut-throat' razor could be sharpened by mechanics or joiners in any part of the world and might, with care, last the owner for his lifetime.

Apart from its handiness, the safety razor was attractive in appearance, making it eminently suitable as a present. Above all, it came in at a time when spending power was increasing among large sections of workpeople.

SCISSORS

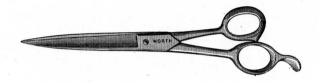

CHAPTER 10

SCISSORS

WHEN considering the probable origin of a tool made with two opposite cutting edges working one against the other, one feels certain that the shear principle was introduced before the scissor-type, for the latter, with its cutting operation dependent on a riveted centre, called for more delicate adjustment during manufacture. Although cutting tools, both of these types represented a great departure from the knife, being adapted specially to cut materials such as hair, wool and woven fabrics.

Shears first appeared in Bronze Age times and they can be traced right through the ages, their modern counterparts being the implements that are to-day used for the hand shearing of sheep. Scissors made during the Roman occupation of Britain were of iron, while scissors manufactured from the same metal, and originating from the period 250 B.C. to 150 B.C., have also been found in France and Germany.

Medieval types of shears are often to be seen inscribed on English grave-stones, denoting, it is believed, the trade of the deceased as being that of a wool-dealer or stapler. Reference to similar inscriptions that appeared on thirteenth-, fourteenth- and fifteenth-century grave slabs was made in an *Historical Account of the Cistercian Abbey of Salley, in Craven, Yorkshire* (J. Harland, London, 1858), from which the following extracts are quoted:

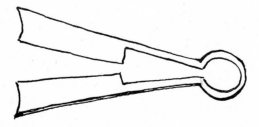

Fig. 54. Shears drawn from a medieval incised grave slab by the author. (*Circa* thirteenth century)

The meaning of the symbol of the shears, notwithstanding all that has been said about it, still remains undetermined. One theory is that they symbolise a wool stapler; another that they are the appropriate symbol of a female.

It was also stated that sharp-pointed shears were essentially for the use of women, while those made square-ended were—

probably those which the clothier used to shear his cloth, i.e. to cut the nap, the blunt ends being intended to preserve the cloth from injury . . . but in a British Museum Manuscript an Abbess is shown cutting off the hair of a Queen with square ended shears.

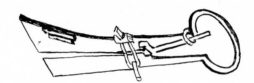

Fig. 55. Florentine cloth-maker's shears

Instances may be cited where swords as well as both sharp and blunt shears were associated with male interments.

There is in my collection a style of scissors made in Sheffield during the nineteenth century for the Persian market. They appear to have been worked by thumb and finger, and when closed they formed a dagger, which was said to be in demand by Eastern ladies to carry in their stockings as a defensive weapon. It is also believed that as carpet-makers, the Persians often asked for scissors that would be suitable for their trade as well as for use as stilettos.

So far as design and craftsmanship are concerned, nineteenth-century scissors are next in importance to spring knives. All the processes involved

---

Fig. 56. Shears and scissors, ancient and modern

(*Top*). Left to right:
Betel scissors, from the Philippines.
Scissors, from Korea.
Shears, from the Dutch East Indies.
Scissors, from China.

(*Bottom*). Left to right:
Nineteenth-century Egyptian scissors.
Scissors made in the nineteenth century in Sheffield for the Persian market. When closed they were used as daggers.
Finely-shaped Siamese shears, suitable for small work.
Ornate scissors, from Benares.
Right, two pairs of Chinese scissors, with contrasting styles of bows.

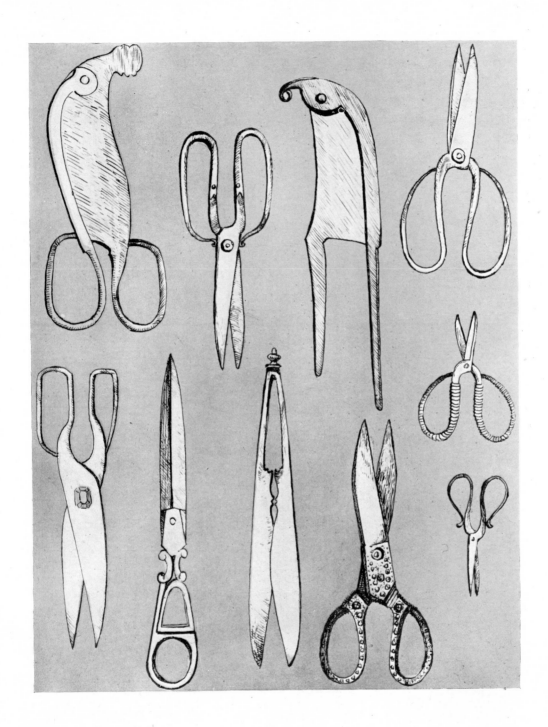

in the manufacture of scissors—forging, boring, hardening, shaping, grinding, filing shanks and bows, putting-together with rivet or screw, polishing and burnishing—were, during that century, carried out by hand. Skilled workmen and women took great pride in their craft, many of them deriving great satisfaction from the results of their dexterity without regard to the monetary reward. Their aim was often the expression of art in the production of articles of everyday use.

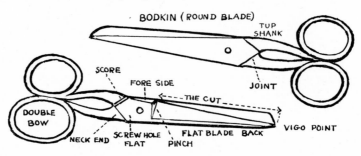

Fig. 57. Sheffield terms for scissors parts

Later, when mass mechanical methods of production became popular in Sheffield, engineering practice had the effect of almost eliminating this highly specialised handcraftsmanship and also greatly reduced manufacturing ranges to only a few basic styles and patterns. Ease of repetition in the production of plain patterns stifled decorative styles and the individual craftsman's expression of his art. This craft in scissor-making is not likely to be rediscovered.

Fig. 58. Sheffield scissors, with details of bows, shanks and blades

Left column, top to bottom:
Flat bow with square reverse shank and bodkin blade.
Wire bow with round tup shank and flat blade.
Wire bow with thread-neck, bat shank and rapier blade.
Bevel bow with thread-neck, bead, sarum shank and bodkin blade.
Flat bow with winged Spanish fiddle joint shank and bodkin blade.
Bevel bow with bead, sarum glass fiddle joint shank and bodkin blade.
Wire bow with square sarum shank and bodkin blade.

Right column, top to bottom:
Fluted bow with bead-neck, sarum, square shank and flat blade.
Flat bow with winged Spanish three-fluted shank and flat blade.
Wire bow with thread-neck sarum shank and flat blade.
Wire bow with reverse glass fiddle joint shank and flat blade.
Wire bow with neb sarum square shank and flat blade.
Wire bow with thread-neck bat shank and flat blade.
Flat bow with winged reverse square neb swamp joint shank and flat blade.

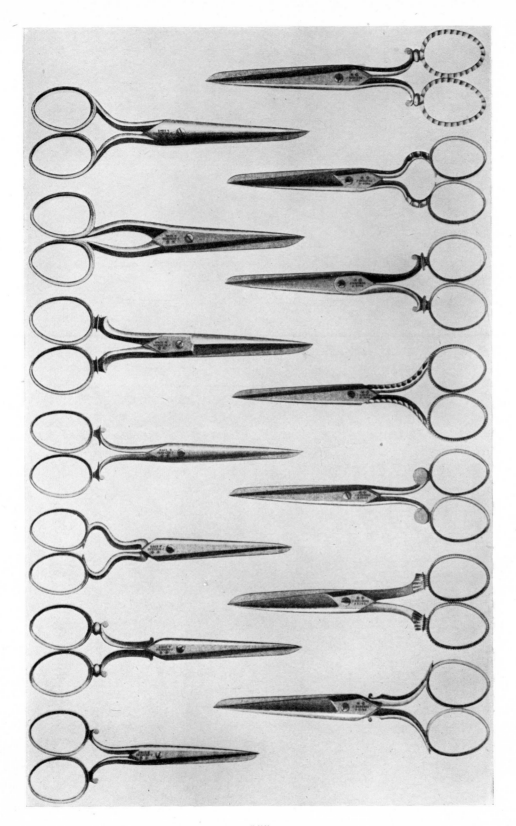

Several of the Cutlery showcases in Sheffield City Museum, are representative of the ornamental styles of scissors that were made for display in the Great Exhibition of 1851, and it seems hardly possible that such fine craftsmanship can ever be surpassed. These scissors, made by local people with none of the precision tools of the present-day worker, were produced by the long experience of hand and eye.

Nineteenth-century scissors were numerous both in size and style. For bows, there was a choice of fluted, flat, wire, bevel or bevel-curl, while there was an even greater variety in shanks, including bead-neck, winged Spanish, thread-neck, square sarum, reverse glass, fiddle joint, common tup, square reverse, round tup, leaf sarum or fluted beaded with curl swamp joint. Blades were described as being either flat, bodkin or rapier.

Some of the special types included folding pocket scissors, tailors' trimmers with side-bent shank, tailors' shears, cockade barbers', lamp-trimmers' and buttonhole scissors. In the field of surgical scissors, there were special patterns for dissecting, which were made either with or without probe points, as well as angular, rowelling and apothecaries' scissors.

An unusual type of scissors that was produced in the nineteenth century and marked 'F. J. Thomas, Coventry', was made specially for the use of anglers. These scissors were designed to hold open the mouth of a fish while extracting the hook. Rows of serrations along the outer edges of both blades prevented slipping, while a spacer bar kept the blades open at the desired width. The other edges were sharpened in the normal fashion.

Fig. 59. Sheffield scissors, including special types

(*Top*). Left to right:
Wire bow with square swamp joint shank and flat blade.
Flat bow with reverse, glass shank and rapier blade.
Flat bow with winged Spanish neb swamp shank and rapier blade.
Fluted bow with winged Spanish shank and rapier blade.
Bevel bow with curl for wing Spanish fiddle joint shank and flat blade.
Bevel bow with double wing, quaker shank and rapier blade.

(*Bottom*). (Top row, left to right):
Folding nail scissors.
Draper's waistcoat pocket size scissors.
Draper's waistcoat scissors, or small pair for nurses.
Buttonhole scissors with screw to regulate size of hole.
Ordinary buttonhole scissors.
(Bottom row, left to right):
Flower gatherers.
Two pairs of vine scissors.
Fancy pattern nail scissors.
Fine-point embroidery scissors.

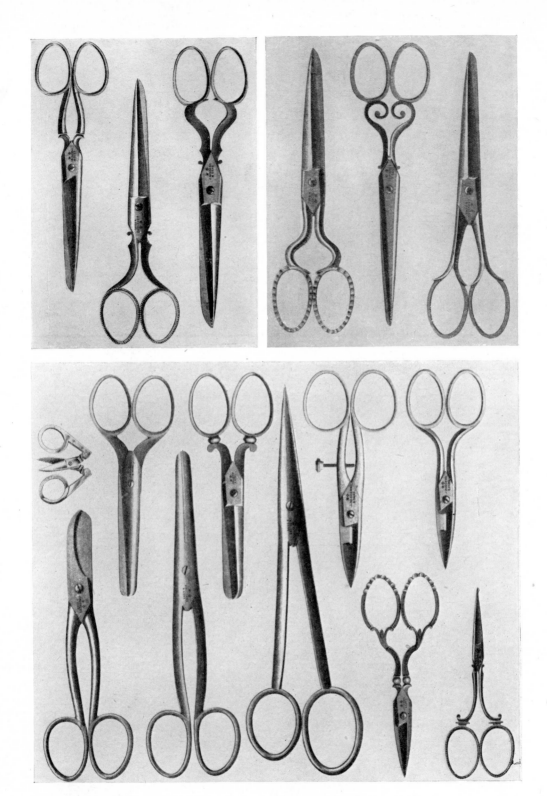

METHODS OF CARRYING CUTLERY
PACKING AND PACKAGING
HARDWOOD CONTAINERS

CHAPTER 11

METHODS OF CARRYING CUTLERY
PACKING AND PACKAGING
HARDWOOD CONTAINERS

EVEN in the Stone Age men found it uncomfortable to carry their knives without a sheath of some kind, and it is most probable that the earliest covering for a flint cutting tool was made of hide. One or two such knives have been discovered with sheaths; that described on p. 26 had a well-preserved covering, a clever combination of a number of simple materials affixed to a girdle. This left its owner free to carry other weapons.

The dagger that Tutankhamen carried and which was found in his tomb was contained in a fine sheath that was as important and as valuable as the knife itself. In the Bronze Age, surgeons kept their instruments in leather cases.

From the later period of the Roman invasion of Britain, a number of folding or shut knives—similar in size and shape to the modern pocket knife—have been unearthed, and may be seen in museums at York and Cirencester. As the handle of a knife of this type folded over the blade to protect the edge, there was no need for a sheath. The knife was probably carried in the fold of the owner's toga.

There is evidence from Viking and Saxon times that the *scramasax* was carried at the belt. The smaller sizes made this knife handy for eating with, but they were not too small for use in defence or attack.

There may be room for argument as to whether the Sheffield 'thwytel' that Chaucer's pilgrim in the fourteenth century 'bare in his hose' was either suspended by a cord from the owner's neck, resting inside his singlet, or kept in his leg covering. Both the Scot and the Gurkha found the stocking suitable for housing knives and other articles.

By the fifteenth century, the table knife had taken that historic stride which removed any suspicion as to whether it was a weapon or an eating implement. The 'point' of the knife was at this time beginning to assume a roundness in the place of its former dagger shape, and table knives were then being kept in cases of leather, ivory or wood, stood upright on their 'points'.

L

The inclusion of a fork in a case with a number of knives during this century not only marked the advent of the fork, but also serves to remind us of the eating habits of our medieval ancestors and explains why the finger bowl and the table napkin figured so prominently at banquets in ancient days.

The three-piece set—knife, fork and spoon contained in one case—was also introduced during the fifteenth century for the convenience of its owner, either in his home or when travelling. In shape, these cases were reminiscent of the traditional form of sheath that was carried at the girdle.

Two centuries later, the effect of the more settled living conditions and growth of trade with foreign countries was reflected in the richer materials being imported to furnish the homes of a growing middle class. Eastern hardwoods, particularly mahogany, rosewood and ebony, were being made into cabinets, chests-of-drawers, sideboards, tables, chairs and clock cases. Table ware of many kinds became as varied and almost as valuable as personal jewellery, except, of course, with the peasant class. Cutlery was then looked upon as a necessity in any well-furnished home.

By the eighteenth century, the era of the finely designed furniture of Chippendale, Sheraton and Hepplewhite, no dining-room was complete without its sideboard, which had one or two drawers to hold cloths and table napkins, with cupboards for wine. Probably to accentuate the importance of the sideboard in the dining-room, it became the fashion for a polished wood urn to be placed at each end of it. The original purpose of these urns is not clear to-day, but at a later stage some were adapted with metal linings as tea urns, while others were fitted with upright racks to hold knives, forks and spoons (Fig. 60).

The better-known cutlery holder of this period was always referred to as a 'knife-box', even though it also held an assortment of forks and spoons as well as knives. These knife-boxes were usually of square section with a shaped moulded front and sloping lid. Generally small in size, they were supplied in pairs—one for each end of the sideboard. Those shown in Fig. 60 have applied pierced silver mounts, are finely inlaid and held four dozen articles stood on end. They are credited to the year 1770.

This container gave rise to the saying that was popular many years ago—'you must have spent the night in a knife-box', a maxim that was usually applied to those who were exceptionally quick-witted or unusually sharp in repartee.

By the twentieth century the cutlery cabinet branch of the wood-working industry had developed to the extent that it called for large factories producing nothing but cases, chests and tables to hold cutlery and plate. To-day, a well-made case may be more expensive than its contents.

With the increased purchasing power brought about by higher wages and the development of social amenities bringing better hygienic and aesthetic conditions, the nineteenth century saw a marked advance in the demand for table ware.

Initially, the necessity for the possession of cutlery, which would be kept in the drawer of the kitchen table, meant that people were satisfied to

Fig. 60. Cutlery containers. Left, a knife urn of the eighteenth century, and right, a pair of knife boxes, *circa* 1770

buy knives, forks and spoons unboxed, but it was not long before there was a growing call for well-wrapped goods at the point of purchase. Later, cardboard boxes containing half a dozen knives were introduced. These appealed to the tidy-minded ironmonger and cutler, both as a showcase and as a container that could be handed to the customer. These boxes also meant that knives could be kept in a clean condition while in the retailer's shop.

By the middle of the last century, cardboard box making was becoming an established trade and storekeepers, merchants and retailers overseas took quickly to the new idea of packaged cutlery, often indenting their orders with the provision that all goods should be boxed in small quantities and labelled attractively. Even so, cardboard box making was not mentioned as a trade in the Sheffield Directory of 1845.

The first cardboard boxes made for the Sheffield trade had a cover-paper of what was known as 'Sheffield green flint', which had a hard, glossy surface. In about 1885, these boxes were made by hand, each corner being cut individually with a pair of scissors. Not long after this, plain coloured covering papers were introduced.[1]

The trade in America appears to have taken the initiative in the development of boxed cutlery, and merchants there were large buyers of Sheffield cutlery in cardboard boxes. Thus was started cutlery packaging—a subject that is still of much concern to present-day manufacturers and distributors.

While the printers of the nineteenth century were capable of dealing with the demand for labels by way of copper plates and lithography, then by wood blocks and later still by half-tone blocks and electros, the making of cardboard boxes evolved as a separate trade, for a large variety of small boxes for many different purposes could be produced by the same processes. At the end of the nineteenth century, some of the finest colour printing ever produced by lithography was executed for this purpose. At this time, too, illustrated catalogues were introduced for advertising.

In following years, well-designed coloured leatherettes, in both cloth and paper, superseded leather for covering the wooden boxes, which, made to meet the popular demand, held small quantities of cutlery, usually from six to twenty-four pieces.

Alongside these lower priced boxes grew a demand for cutlery cases to harmonise with the styles of traditional furniture. Mostly made in Sheffield, in both British and foreign hardwoods with french-polished surfaces, these cases contained racks and fittings of pine-wood covered with cloth, velvet or satin. The earliest flat, square cases that followed the upright Sheraton period were usually lined with green or blue baize or cloth, and were most probably London-made, as often were their contents.

As Sheffield came to be regarded as the cutlery centre of the world, a number of cabinet case makers, as they were first known, started business, employing one or two men in each factory to make cases. Women were employed to line the cases.

The Sheffield Directory for 1825 lists twelve firms under the heading of 'Cabinet Case and Strap Makers' as distinct from lists of 'Cabinet Makers' and 'Cabinet Makers and Upholsterers'. In 1828, the same number were included under the slightly extended heading of 'Cabinet Case and

---

[1] From information supplied by Mr. C. H. Lea of Sheffield.

Razor Strop Makers', with 'Strap' changed to 'Strop'. By 1845, the Directory contained a list of thirty-one such firms, with a slightly amended heading—'Cabinet and Razor Case and Strop Manufacturers, (also Pattern Card Makers)'—which showed the growing importance of good quality razors. The razor cases may have been of papier-mâché, but more likely were wooden boxes holding one pair of the better-quality razors.

The bracketed reference to 'Pattern Card Makers' indicates the introduction of a new feature in the cutlery trades. On these cards were stitched samples of pocket knives, razors, table cutlery, scissors and other small articles. They were sent abroad to prospective customers and were used by travellers when soliciting orders from retailers in Britain.[1]

By 1850, cutlery case manufacturers were looked upon as a separate specialised trade that was almost solely concerned with supplying cases to cutlery firms. In recent boom years, large quantities of small cases and large cabinets were being made to hold sufficient cutlery, spoons and forks to lay out a dining table for six, eight, twelve, twenty-four or thirty-six persons. Those for thirty-six might contain 300 or more pieces, including fish and fruit eaters. Larger quantities were supplied in plate chests for officers' regimental messes and clubs.

In the present century, cutlery manufacturers placed orders for hundreds of oak, mahogany and walnut tables, featuring Chippendale, inlaid Sheraton and Hepplewhite sideboards with several drawers to hold nothing but cutlery and table linen. Few of these equalled their traditional originals in either craftsmanship or design; they were, however, mostly skilful reproductions, well-finished from good materials.

It appears that in no other country was produced such a range and quantity of polished wood cases as in England, where Sheffield seems to have been the centre of the trade. London and Birmingham manufacturers produced a few, but these were chiefly smaller or leatherette-covered cases.

The assumption that no other country entered so thoroughly into the manufacture of hardwood cases for cutlery received some support from an investigation, carried out after the Second World War, into the trade in Germany. In 1946, the principals of two of the largest cutlery case firms in Sheffield were appointed to survey the German cutlery case, canteen and cabinet industry. Their sixty-one-page report (*B.I.O.S. Final Report No.*

---

[1] I have some sample cards that were made in 1888. Of very substantial cardboard, they comprise two sheets ⅛ in. thick, hinged at the centre with maroon leather. Measuring 12 in. by 15 in., they are covered with hand-marbled paper on the outside. The inner lining is of white glossy paper covered with a slight chequered pattern. Along the top and bottom are strips of thin maroon leather with the firm's name and trade mark impressed in English gold foil by a brass gilding stamp.

1,135, items 22 and 31, was published by H.M. Stationery Office, London, in 1947).

They reported that in pre-war years the trade consisted mainly of small firms employing not more than twelve workers each; larger concerns were an exception. The quantity of machinery was surprisingly small and poor in quality; in the opinion of the investigators this was due to the fact that hardwood cutlery cabinets were in little demand at any time. In the leatherette-covered case section, however, methods in some instances reflected an improvement on British practice, and they felt it worthy of note that both male and female workers were 'instinctively interested' in turning out 'a neat and beautifully made article, however insignificant the job'. After the war, the shortage of good materials called for much economical and hard work to produce the best possible articles.

Within the boundaries of the modern city of Sheffield are to be seen portions of old mule tracks, packhorse roads and bridges, and fords that were paved with grindstones. These trade routes speak of the days before the advent of carriers' wagons, or carts and coaches for the transport of cutlery, for old tracks are much in evidence in these hilly surroundings, as are walls with toppers of old grindlecowks (stones).

Packmen or chapmen who carried their own packs and wares would ante-date even the mule and packhorse as a means of transport, for although many believe that man was gregarious by instinct, he was ever a wanderer, as archæologists have evidenced from early trails across Europe into Asia and, even earlier, possibly in the opposite direction.

As roads were made, carriers' wagons came into use for the transport of goods and passengers. In 1787, at least twenty carriers are recorded as linking Sheffield with other centres, before the opening of a railway in 1838. In 1820, goods took three or four days to reach London from Sheffield, the first stage of the journey, by wagon to Hull, taking twenty-six hours. At Hull, the consignments of cutlery for London were transferred to a steam packet.

Pickford & Company of Arundel Street, Sheffield, were in 1825 carrying both passengers and goods by land 'per caravan on springs and guarded', in thirty-four hours to their warehouse at Castle Inn, Wood Street, London. By this means Sheffield developed a large trade in cutlery with the capital city.

Sheffield cutlers ensured that their products were well packed to withstand damage during transit. Until the end of the nineteenth century, pocket knives, razors, table knives and scissors were wrapped mostly in dozens, usually in acid-free paper made from locally manufactured rope pulp. Previously, it was the practice to oil the steel parts of all types of cutlery to protect them against damp.

Before 1880, large quantities of cutlery for both home and export customers were packed in casks, which were more easily handled than square packing cases or boxes, for cranes were seldom used in those days. The packer started by arranging the parcels of knives on end round the inside of the cask, to form the first row. The next row was placed inside that, and the process continued until the first layer was complete. The packer then proceeded in the same manner until the top of the cask was reached.

Packing somewhat square parcels inside a round barrel to make a tight firm fit certainly called for more dexterous work than the filling of a square modern packing case. The manufacturers of those casks were described as 'coopers and packing case makers'.

CUTLERY-MAKING
IN LONDON AND THAXTED

CHAPTER 12

CUTLERY-MAKING
IN LONDON AND THAXTED

LONDON cutlers were associated with some kind of fraternity or society as early as 1154 to 1189, and in the thirteenth century their Guild was of considerable importance. At an early stage, the Guild was divided into three distinct sections—blade-makers, cutlers and hafters (assemblers and finishers), and sheath-makers. This sub-division and specialisation developed as the demand arose for articles that were fine in craftsmanship, materials and design.

Grinding and glazing, important processes in the making of every knife, must have been covered by the finishers' section, but it is known that there was much overlapping within the various sections.

The London Cutlers' Guild, which drew up many ordinances and regulations, was often at variance with other guilds. In 1327, the Goldsmiths' Company complained that some of the decorative work effected by the cutlers, for which they felt responsible, was deceptive. At first, they accused the cutlers of covering 'tin and silver so subtlely, and with such sleight, that the same cannot be severed from the tin, and by that means they sell the tin so covered as fine silver, to the great damage and deceit of us and our people'.

Later, goldsmiths claimed the right to assay and the right of search over all cutlery on which gold or silver was worked.

In 1408, London bladesmiths found their business was being interfered with by knives and blades that were being brought in by 'foreign folks from divers parts of England'. These 'foreign folks' were provincials or those not freemen of a company or town.

The London Cutlers' Company, as the Guild was later known, was always on the look-out for inferior cutlery, and a minute of November 26, 1683, recorded that two razors were seized at Bartholomew Fair from Thomas Lawrence. With the help of a Mr. Wordman, from whom he had purchased the razors, Lawrence was able to prove 'that they were Sheffield make, whereupon they were returned to him'. (Razors first appeared in the Sheffield Company's records in 1680–1.)

171

Custom House books of the reign of Henry VIII (1509–47) record the importation of Continental cutlery, mainly of French and German origin. There were times, however, when such imports were prohibited, as in 1550 and again in 1563, when large quantities were being brought in from Flanders and the Low Countries. Restrictions were next imposed on the import of cutlery in 1628 and 1641.

Sheffield in the sixteenth century also became a strong competitor to London, particularly in the capital city's foreign markets, for Sheffield knives were being exported from Liverpool and Chester as early as 1586. The south Yorkshire town was in 1614 also sending cutlery to most parts of England.

Strife marked the relations of London and Sheffield cutlers in the seventeenth century, when London manufacturers complained of 'English Foreigners' caught hawking their goods in the city's streets and highways.

Sheffield manufacturers were also charged with counterfeiting some London marks, although this was at times done to the order of London merchants, who benefited when well-made Sheffield knives bore the marks of the capital's cutlers. London merchants were also not averse to stamping Spanish and other marks on their blades, while Sheffield- and Birmingham-made knives, swords and daggers were often on seizure found to have been stamped with London marks. London cutlers were in fact prosecuted on occasions for making up provincial knives and stamping them with their own marks.

The use of London marks was officially sanctioned in Sheffield as late as 1785, but the Cutlery Trade Act of 1819 decreed that articles of cutlery manufactured elsewhere than in the capital must not be marked with the words 'London' or 'London Made'.

The latter part of the eighteenth century saw the decline of London's position in the cutlery-making industry, although manufacturers there carried on valiantly with some of their finer qualities until the beginning of the nineteenth century. Indeed, a few Sheffield craftsmen, particularly forgers, were induced to work in London, mainly to help keep alive the butcher's knife trade.

It may be fairly claimed that by 1840, however, Sheffield manufacturers made almost all the cutlery that was then produced in the United Kingdom, including that sold by London merchants, who marked Sheffield products with their own trade marks and street addresses, but omitting the word 'London'. On the other hand, Sheffield at no time became a serious competitor with either London or Birmingham in the production of swords or small arms.

Thaxted

Thaxted, Essex, with its fourteenth-century Town Hall, which was probably built by the cutlers, and an ancient hamlet of thatched cottages fringing a common that is still known as Cutlers' Green, is a fine example of an old English country town before the craftsman turned his back on rural surroundings and allowed himself to be herded with his fellows into industrial centres. At the time of the Norman Conquest, the population of Thaxted comprised about 500 families.

In 1610, Camden described Thaxted as 'a little mercate town seated pleasantly upon a high rising hill'. To-day, Thaxted is situated at the terminus of a single-line light railway and it is interesting to note that at Cutlers' Green, after which one of the nearby stations was named, the craft of cutlery was carried on as long ago as 1255 by men who, after the fashion of the time, were also husbandmen.

Fairs were held on the green from the reign of Edward II (1307–27), originally on the Feast of St. Luke, but, as the number of cutlers increased, the Feast of St. Lawrence, their patron, became the favoured day.

In the main street, wide enough to hold booths and stalls to form a good-sized market, stands the Cutlers' Guild Hall, a fine timber-and-plaster building, while nearby are a number of ancient houses of similar style. Smiths, cutlers and armourers had their dwellings and workshops between the Guild Hall and Cutlers' Green.

One of the chapels in the large Parish Church was dedicated to the patron saint of the cutlers, St. Lawrence, who gave his name to their Guild. This was a trade guild rather than a religious or charitable fraternity, as was the local Guild of St. John. Within ten days of the death of a member of the Cutlers' Guild, it was the custom to hold twenty or more masses, the members attending each paying a small sum for the mass and the candles that they burned. In 1473, a cutler bequeathed that the rent from a plot of land was to be applied 'towards performing my orbit requiem masses in Thaxted Parish Church'.

John ffan, a cutler who was a churchwarden in the sixteenth century, was responsible for issuing the candles and also looked after the Guild Chapel of St. Lawrence. He came from a long line of cutler-husbandmen and after his death he, too, was buried in the 'crossing' of the chapel, as were his fellow Guild members.

There were close connections between the cutlers of London and Thaxted; the London Husting Roll of 1287 records the name of 'Richard de Taxted', a hafter (Thaxted was spelt as the name was then pronounced).

In 1309, 'Adam de Taxted' was recorded as having opened his own cutler's shop in 'Chepe ward', London, 'on Thursday before 2 February'. Described as a 'coteler', he was 'admitted to the freedom of the City before the Mayor and Aldermen, and paid a fee of two Mark, being resident in the ward of Chepe'. It is a fair assumption that, having learned his trade in his native town of Thaxted, Adam obtained his freedom, probably by purchase, before he could open his shop in London.

London merchants supplied Thaxted workers with raw materials, at any rate for their best work, for the City Guild, in 1462, recorded that a cutler of Thaxted, 'an Essex town where cutlery has long flourished', was allowed to buy $3\frac{1}{2}$ lb. of ivory at $1s.$ per lb. On another occasion, a cutler from the same locality bought a whole tusk that weighed about 53 lb.

Although Thaxted bladesmiths, sheathers, gold-beaters, furbishers and grinders made a large variety of cutlery, including knives, daggers, swords and surgeons' instruments, all of which were executed with a high degree of craftsmanship, they were in the fifteenth and sixteenth centuries also engaged in farming and husbandry.

So far as can be ascertained, there are extant no specimens of knives bearing Thaxted marks. Silver spoons and other domestic articles made in the Essex town were mentioned in a will dated 1505, and the manufacture of cutlery was carried on at Thaxted in a small way until the seventeenth century. The two crossed swords, rose and fetterlock that compose the arms of Thaxted date probably from 1554.

The Thaxted cutlery fraternity must have enjoyed a status of repute in their town, for the names of people registered as having purchased, leased or rented land between the fourteenth and sixteenth centuries are variously described in old deeds as following the 'trade or mystery of coteler, sheather and hafter'.

Family surnames have been mentioned in records continuously for hundreds of years, and widows appear to have carried on the trade of their deceased husbands, as was the practice also in Sheffield.

A Thaxted cutlery-making family that was well-known as early as 1377 was that of Aleyne, descendants of whom left their native town for London. One of them, who became a Lord Mayor of London, bought land from the King, and in 1544 left a collar of gold for the use of succeeding Lord Mayors, and 500 marks for the purchase of a stock of sea coal. A member of the same family, Edward Alleyn, founded Dulwich College in 1619.

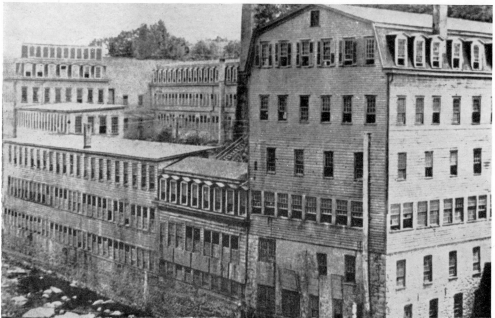

Fig. 61. (*Top*). The Cutlers' Guild Hall at Thaxted, the ancient cutlery town of Essex. (*Bottom*). The New York Knife Works, Walden, U.S.A., which was established by Sheffield craftsmen in the nineteenth century

CUTLERY IN FRANCE
AND GERMANY

CHAPTER 13

CUTLERY IN FRANCE AND GERMANY

FRANCE from the early Middle Ages to comparatively recent times was an important cutlery-making country. Most of the prehistoric periods were, in fact, named after French districts, and are now accepted by scholars all over the world—Chellean, Acheulean, Mousterian, Aurignacian and Magdalenian. In later times, Paris, Thiers and Châtellerault have been the principal cutlery centres of France.

From Châtellerault came Camille Pagé, the cutlery historian, who spent a lifetime compiling the history of cutlery that he published in France in six volumes during the period 1896 to 1904. He was a member of a family that produced master cutlers from the sixteenth century onwards; it was still flourishing in 1924, when I corresponded with Mme. Pagé, his widow.

Sheffield Museum authorities in 1932 acquired the whole of the collection on which Pagé based his history, a collection that comprised about 1,000 specimens of early cutlery.

Although French makers produced great quantities of cutlery in well-proportioned styles and with decorative features that were second to none in the world, they do not appear to have developed an export trade to any extent, as did manufacturers in other countries, a factor which probably accounts for the moderate influence that French cutlery had on the markets of the world.

In the nineteenth century, some 18,000 workpeople were employed in the industry at Thiers; next in importance came Langres and Nogent, followed, respectively, by Paris and Châtellerault. Toulouse and a number of other French towns made no small contribution to the craft. As early as 1261, Paris ordinances showed cutlery to be of some importance.

Thiers, a picturesque town in the valley of the River Durolle, has been the chief centre of French cutlery production from early times. The town possesses a church that was built in 575, an abbey dating from 742 and much domestic architecture of medieval origin. There have been master cutlers of Thiers since 1568.

As cutlery-making centres, Paris, from whence came the most artistic

French cutlery, Langres, Nogent and Châtellerault have been of lesser note than Thiers, certainly as regards quantity, if not quality. The output of the cutlers of Thiers and the surrounding district was three times as great as the combined total of all the other French cutlery-producing towns.

Thiers obtained its commercial freedom in the thirteenth century, and by the fourteenth century was exporting to Italy, Spain and the Low Countries the goods that it could not dispose of in French markets. In 1336, duties and taxes were being levied on knives made at Thiers. The trade of the local cutlers greatly expanded at the close of the fifteenth century and the beginning of the sixteenth century, owing to large orders from Spain, following the discovery of America.

To-day, almost all the cutlery of France is produced at Thiers and the small cutlery towns that stretch along the banks of the rivers that flow through the nearby valleys. There are some 400 manufacturing firms in Thiers, out of a district total of 1,200, each of which employs anything from twenty to 400 workers. It is estimated that between 16,000 and 18,000 workpeople earn their living from the local cutlery trade.

In 1942, the town was occupied by an expedition of 300 German S.S. troops. The occupying force was wiped out in 1944, and by 1947 the export tonnage of Thiers cutlery had doubled the figure for 1938, indicating a quick recovery. During 1947, a total of 4,500 tons of fine steel was made up into cutlery.

In 1948, the exports of local manufacturers to French colonial territories were almost equal in quantity to those sent to foreign countries. The colonial markets mostly took low-priced utility goods, foreign buyers receiving a smaller tonnage of higher-grade patterns, which, because of the greater cost, was valued at 60 per cent. of the total exports.

By March of the following year, M. J. J. Carburol, President of the Chambre Syndicale de la Coutellerie, in an article in the Paris edition of the *New York Herald Tribune*, was able to say that Thiers had completed its economic recovery. The retail prices of its products were twelve times higher than what they had been before the war, an increase which M. Carburol thought compared favourably with the prices of controlled food-stuffs.

At present, both manufacturers and craftsmen are expressing a strong inclination for traditional qualities of craftsmanship and design. This is coupled with a desire to keep abreast of modern developments, as has been demonstrated by the setting up of a National Technical School. Attached to it is a cutlery laboratory, where testing facilities are made available to local manufacturers. Thiers cutlers to-day use many up-to-date mechanical forges and automatic sharpening and polishing machines.

The rivers that traverse the valleys around Thiers provide the motive power for the local cutlery industry. There are 140 dams within a two-and-a-half mile stretch of the Durolle, and between them are the waterfalls that have the natural advantage of the river's 1,000-ft. drop in altitude.

Only ten of the old water-wheels that abounded along the river banks are still used for the making of cutlery, and more than 95 per cent. of the

Fig. 62. (Left). Scissors-maker at Solingen, Germany. (Right). Cutlery factories at Thiers, France

power that is needed by the local cutlers is provided by the dams of Auvergne, whose water turbines range from 20 h.p. up to 80 h.p., according to the height of the falls.

M. Carburol has claimed that Thiers was the 'first industrial centre in the world to use high grade stainless steel with chrome and nickel'. Whether this implies its use in cutlery-making was not stated, and no data were given to substantiate the claim.

A hundred years ago, Thiers sought trade in Britain, and a number of cutlers who displayed their products in the Great Exhibition of 1851 and the International Exhibition of 1862, both of which were held in London, gained medals of merit. In 1851, Thiers cutlery manufacturers were importing steel from England—presumably Sheffield—and Germany.

Germany and Central Europe

Knives and other cutlery articles were being made in Central Europe in ancient times. The craftsmen of that area must have benefited from the fact that the great plain that stretched from the English Channel to the Urals encouraged travel and the intermixing of Western and Eastern influences, for in very early periods Central Europe was visited by peoples of Equatorial Africa, South African, Egyptian, Latin, Roman, Nordic and Gaelic origins.

Invading armies also penetrated mid-Europe, effecting a further interchange of ideas, materials and craftsmen. These contacts of one race with another are reflected in styles of architecture as well as in the goods that were produced. Cutlers in some of the old European towns credit the Romans with having established their industry, for the Roman armies that overran Europe were accompanied by men skilled in the making of knives and they passed their trade on to others in the occupied countries.

Roman sword- and dagger-makers, whose work called for great skill, provided a sound traditional influence when the demand arose later for cutlery for the huntsman and for the table. Nations and colonial territories that are young in development lack this traditional skill in industry and the high standards of quality that the early craftsmen of the older civilisations bequeathed to succeeding generations.

Central European workmanship has nearly always been of the highest order, but its products have sometimes been criticised when qualities of raw material, notably steel, and standards of craftsmanship have been sacrificed to meet price competition. (Not that cutlers in other parts of the world have unblemished reputations in this respect!)

Many Continental towns and cities of necessity made their own knives and tools from early times. Their armourers and forgers provided daggers, short swords and pruning knives, in addition to larger instruments of warfare and agriculture. Toledo, Madrid, Seville and, possibly, Barcelona in Spain, with numerous towns of France, Belgium and Holland, established reputations in the field of general metalwork in medieval days. Ancient cutlers of Florence, Rome, Milan and other Italian towns competed with the craftsmen of Germany's old cutlery centres.

Existing German records show that cutlery was being manufactured in Augsburg in 1346, when the forging of blades was controlled by regulations. In 1551, it is recorded that apprentices were fined for absence from work, unless they were ill. By the seventeenth and possibly early eighteenth centuries, cutlery was no longer being produced in Berlin, Cologne, Heidelberg, Mannheim, Mayence, Munich or Nuremberg, although in many of these and other German towns, guilds had been established in the Middle Ages, with certain powers and concessions granted by their respective communities.

Tuttlingen still has a reputation for the manufacture of cutlery, but knives are no longer made in Hamburg, a port once renowned for its high standards of razor grinding and for the exports of large quantities of cutlery.

The small West German town of Wetzlar built up a large export trade in whetstones for razors and surgical instruments. Quarried locally in two varieties, old rock and new rock, these were sought by Sheffield cutlery manufacturers fifty-five years' ago, and continued in demand until artificial stones came into fashion. Wetzlar stones measured about 8 in. by 3 in. by $1\frac{3}{4}$ in. thick, with the upper—and more important—half being of a dark cream colour, similar to the lithographic stones used by printers, which came from the same district. Both types of stone had the same fine texture.

The cutlers' craft was well established in Austria in the year 1408, with the town of Steyr as the centre, where knives and other cutlery were made right into the nineteenth century, when some 1,000 cutlery workers were employed. The Austrian cutlery industry was never large and only a small quantity of its finished products were exported.

Solingen

Solingen, said to have been started on its course of cutlery-making by workers of Damascus in the twelfth century, has long been looked upon as the principal competitor to Sheffield. Solingen cutlers were making fine-quality swords in the fourteenth century and by 1472 there were three separate guilds, the earliest of which was established in 1401, for grinders and temperers. The Finishers' and Knife Makers' Guild was formed as a separate corporation in 1571.

A guild concerned with the making of 'little knives'—apparently an off-shoot from the Swordsmiths' Guild—existed in the sixteenth century and was contemporary with the earliest known Sheffield ordinances.

Mechanical hammers driven by water-wheels were used for forging in Solingen during the sixteenth century, long before blades were made in that manner elsewhere. In fact, hand forging persisted in Sheffield until well in the present century, although it should be mentioned that Sheffield cutlers had harnessed water power for grinding and for working iron into rods at about the same time, if not a little earlier, as the development of drop forging in Solingen.

An attempt that was made to prohibit the use of 'goffed' blades in Solingen in 1687 shows that the hand forgers strongly objected to the change to machinery. Some of the finer qualities associated with handwork were being debased by mass manufacture, which also tended to lower the standard of the finished article.

The best examples of German craftsmanship, however, equalled those of any other cutlery-making country. Up to the outbreak of the Second World War, Germany's cutlery-making centres—such as Solingen and Ramscheid—were not only exporting vast quantities of low-priced cutlery, but in their better articles were second only to Sheffield in the quality of steel from which the blades were forged. For some time, I had in my possession a Solingen pocket knife label that bore the legend, 'Made from Sheffield Steel'.

On the other hand, such was the reputation of Hamburg razor-grinders, whose proficiency in craftsmanship was not surpassed anywhere in the world, that Sheffield razor-makers often sent their products to Hamburg for the final processes of grinding and polishing. These blades were returned to Sheffield, often for export to other world markets, marked 'Made in Sheffield: Ground in Hamburg'.

In 1800, the Solingen cutlery trade employed more than 3,000 work-people, excluding sword-makers. Steam power was introduced there about 1850, some thirty years after its development in Sheffield, and by 1908 the number of workers engaged in the Solingen industry had risen to about 10,000, comprising 3,300 pocket knife cutlers, 3,000 scissor-makers, 2,000 employed on table cutlery and 2,000 on razor-making.

The introduction of electrical energy had the effect of decentralising the concentration of workers in factories, many of them finding it possible to set up workshops in their suburban homes. This trend is in contrast with the general development of electricity in Sheffield and has helped to minimise Solingen's blackened depressed areas.

Most of the modern improvements in the Solingen industry were introduced under strict regulations, accompanied by sanitary standards, apprenticeship training schemes and fixed price lists that were rigidly enforced. At the beginning of the twentieth century, Solingen workers held a respected position in their community and were noteworthy for their intelligence and independent outlook.

After the 1939–45 World War, a team of Sheffield cutlery manu-facturers investigated the Solingen industry on behalf of H.M. Government, issuing their report in February, 1947.[1] Their enquiries did not include non-ferrous spoons and forks or safety razors.

The president of the Solingen Chamber of Commerce told the team that before the war the number of local cutlery-making concerns totalled

[1] British Intelligence Objective Sub-Committee, *Report*, 1,002/1947 (H.M. Stationery Office.)

1,200, of which more than 1,000 employed fewer than twenty-five or more workers; 5–10 per cent. of the companies also owned factories outside the Solingen area.

Pre-war sales of Solingen cutlery, including razor blades and surgical instruments, were shown in the report as having been:

	1928	1936
	£ Million	
German sales	£6½	£5⅕
German exports	£3½	£2⅔
Solingen district sales	£5½	£4½
Solingen district exports	£3	£2¼

After visiting thirty-one factories and interviewing the principals, the Sheffield cutlery team reported that most of the skilled work—forging and so on—was performed by male workers. Their rate of pay, based on the 1946 rate of exchange (RM.40 to the £1) worked out at 6d. to 9d. per hour. Female workers were paid at less than half that rate.

The workers were said to be still proud of their skill, and the workshops were invariably found to be clean, well-lit and airy, each man keeping his bench or machine in good condition. Most of the machines, however—even those of comparatively recent manufacture—were old in design.

None of the manufacturing methods observed by the team demonstrated any great departure from Sheffield processes, except in minor details concerning the production of scissors and pocket knives.

While heat treatment—hardening and tempering—was in some cases carried out in modern furnaces under pyrometric control, by far the greater proportion in 1946 depended on the experience and skill of the worker in judging, for instance, temper by the colour of the steel.

Contrary to English custom, all grindstones and glazers were seen to revolve towards the worker—even in the grinding of table, butchers', kitchen and pocket knives. The grinder sat in front of the stone, using a 'flat stick' against his knees for large work.

It was reported that in no case was a machine seen to be efficiently guarded, either mechanically or electrically, according to accepted British practice.

German manufacturers in their best qualities of pre-war cutlery always exhibited fine standards of finish and attention to detail. The cutlery produced in 1946, while not equal to the standards of ten years earlier, was said to be fairly good and low in price.

Germany was not the only country whose cutlery suffered as a result of the depredations of war. Several post-war factors also contributed to reduce the quality of some of the cutlery-producing processes in the British industry, and many Sheffield manufacturers and craftsmen were in the first few years after the war disappointed at what they could offer. This lowering of traditionally high standards was no doubt largely brought about by the lack of experienced craftsmen, many of whom had died or changed their occupations during the war, and the fact that young people had neither been trained in nor taught to appreciate the traditional standards of quality.

The pressing demand for large quantities of standardised patterns to meet the needs of cutlery-starved world markets also served to lower standards. Comparatively small production capacities set against huge shipping orders often resulted in hurried and careless work.

That the quality of German cutlery was low after the war was confirmed by an experience of the firm of which I am a partner. A foreign customer had asked for a quotation for export, and on viewing the samples of the firm's work, placed an order. He had come to Sheffield after having rejected the poor quality of cutlery offered in Germany.

The years 1951 to 1953, however, have witnessed a great recovery in standards of craftsmanship in Europe, together with a resurgence of competition from Continental cutlery-makers in Sheffield's export markets.

Scandinavia

Although Scandinavia was responsible for some of the finest quality Stone Age implements, the northern countries have had only a slight influence on the world's cutlery markets in more recent times. Probably this is because those nations are not very industrialised and export some of their best and most useful metals to other countries.

The delightful little town of Eskilstuna, the only cutlery town in Sweden—or for that matter in Scandinavia—has a reputation for producing quality cutlery, but the quantity manufactured there has never been very large. When I visited Sweden in 1938, most of the table knives displayed in retail shops were fitted with blades imported from Germany, as also were those seen in Norway. Thirty years earlier, Sweden imported a fair quantity of blades ready for hafting from Sheffield.

One type of pen and pocket knife characteristic of Scandinavia, although found also in Germany, was fitted with ornamental scales. It was finely decorated in coloured patinations and thinly applied enamels, reminiscent of niello black lines and coloured fillings on silver or silver gilt. Many of the designs were based on Louis XV styles.

THE UNITED STATES
OF AMERICA

CHAPTER 14

THE UNITED STATES OF AMERICA

THE early pioneers who opened up the vast areas of North America to the settlers were in the main dependent for their knives and tools upon the industry of Sheffield, for cutlery manufacturing was not started in America until the beginning of the nineteenth century, with the earliest firms sited chiefly in Connecticut.

There, the Meriden Cutlery Company was founded in 1835, with the manufacture of pocket knives as its main item. In 1845, the Empire Knife Company of West Winstead produced knives and razors, while the Miller Brothers made pocket knives in 1850, and the Southington Cutlery Company followed with knives and razors. These firms, along with the William Rogers Manufacturing Company (Hartford) and possibly seven others, had their factories in the same State of Connecticut.

The next state of importance in the manufacture of cutlery was Massachusetts, with the John Russell Company, claiming to have started in 1834, making table cutlery and said to have employed about 450 workers between the years 1890 and 1900. The Torry Razor Company was also situated in this State—at Worcester.

The Clauss Shear Company, founded in 1877 at Toledo, Ohio, specialised in bread knives, but also built up a reputation overseas in later years for scissors. Towards the end of the nineteenth century, the Hatch Cutlery Company, South Milwaukee, had a large factory that was engaged in the production of a wide variety of scissor patterns and knives.

American cutlers imported raw materials for their work through New York and Brooklyn, where one or two cutlery manufacturers were also established in the nineteenth century.

Cutlery made in North America—as has been pointed out by other writers—closely resembled that produced in England. American manufacturers, in fact, copied Sheffield styles. A notable exception was the Bowie knife, the only nineteenth-century knife of a true American origin. (The development of this knife and the life of Colonel Jim Bowie, who invented it, are described later in this chapter.)

Sheffield's great influence upon the trend of American cutlery is evidenced by the fact that manufacturers in Connecticut found it worthwhile, as early as 1849, to employ craftsmen from Sheffield, who specialised in different processes. One of these men, James Roberts, Senior, when writing to his children in Sheffield from Waterville, Waterbury, Connecticut, in September, 1849, described how he obtained work with the Waterville Company on the production of pocket knives.[1]

Roberts, who was living in Sheffield Street, mentioned that his son James was working with him and had recently injured his hand under a stamp, or mechanical hammer, that cut pocket knife springs at one stroke. (It is noteworthy that American cutlers used the drop hammer in the middle of the nineteenth century; their industry had only been born a few years previously. This early use of machinery was probably much in advance of the general practice in Sheffield.)

In the same letter, Roberts was glad to hear that his friends in Sheffield had plenty of work, but noted that wages had not improved in England. That was not his experience in Connecticut, for he was then earning $7 a week, and he added that if his daughter Mary could obtain work whetting knives she would receive about $4 a week.

The company that employed him had a capital of $100,000 and was then the largest spring knife manufactory in America, with the best workshops he had ever seen. All the scales and springs were machine-made, the processes of drilling and boring also being effected by power. The employers provided soap for washing when the workers went to dinner and when they left the factory at night—a novelty so far as the Sheffielders were concerned.

The Waterville Company employed about 100 setters-in, seventeen or eighteen blade-makers and probably thirty grinders, with a man to kindle the fires and another to sweep the shops once a day.

Roberts sent messages to old friends in Sheffield, including one to Matthew Dodworth, well known to Sheffield manufacturers as a maker of tools for cutlery production. He also referred to his Chartist friends in Sheffield, to whom he promised to write further when he was better acquainted with the politics of the new country.

In February, 1850, Roberts mentioned that for six weeks he had been cutting up stag horn for scales at a wage of $1.50 a day. He added that there was no limit to the amount of work available and that his daughter Mary, who a few months later was to marry a Mr. Thomas Bradley, was now working in the company's warehouse.

A change in conditions was reported in February, 1852, when Roberts

[1] Based on extracts from letters in the possession of Mr. Eric Preston of Sheffield, a descendant of James Roberts.

wrote that the firm had told the Sheffield workpeople that they must find all their own files and other tools or 'go about their business'. Sixteen of the Sheffield men decided to form their own company, each of them putting down $200. Later they were joined by other Sheffield craftsmen, and it was agreed that all must be workers, as they were determined not to carry shareholders who were investors only.

The new firm was launched in 1853 under the style of the New York Knife Company of Walden, Orange County, N.Y. (and of Wallkill River Works). At this time, Roberts' son-in-law, Bradley, was working in his own home pinning in two-blade pearl pen knives. His son, T. J. Bradley, was later to become a President of the New York Knife Company, and when he died in 1920 he was a Senator for New York. It is believed that the company did not continue long after this. Fig. 61 illustrates the company's works.

Bradley was company President between 1867 and 1870, and in his first year he invited workpeople from Sheffield to come to the United States, bringing their hammers, small tools and anvils. A fine blade-forger was particularly sought. Two years later, in August, 1869, he made another appeal for Sheffield workers, asking especially for Alfred Elshaw, an employee of Wade and Butchers, who had expressed a desire to work in America.

On a later occasion, Bradley referred to a draft for £7 6s., which was to cover the cost of corkscrews, worth £1, with the remaining £6 6s. for a blade-forger. He stated that George Wostenholm, who had called at their Walden factory before returning to England, had remarked at the good progress made by the Sheffielders in their enterprise.

In his last letter as President, Bradley sought two or three stag cutters who would be prepared to pay their own passages—they were promised steady work. Men in other branches of the cutlery industry were also required.

Later, in 1877 or 1879, a number of Sheffield workmen, including William Himsworth, a razor-grinder, and John Hibbard, an etcher, were sent for by an American firm. They took with them their tools and a tank of Sheffield water for hardening, as the American cutlers were said to be experiencing difficulty with the quality of their blades. (It is likely, however, that the acknowledged poor quality of the American blades was due to experimental work in using stamps, or machines, on steel that was intended to be hand-forged.)

John Hibbard later returned to Sheffield, living to be well over eighty years of age and dying about the year 1940. William Himsworth, who also returned after employment in Meriden, Bridgeport, and later at Southington, Connecticut, lived in Sheffield until 1908.

The Bowie Knife

The Saxon *scramasax* and the Sheffield 'whittle' that followed it have been described in earlier chapters as all-purpose knives. In later times, their descendant has been the Bowie knife of the United States, which occupied a unique position even in pioneering days when long-range weapons using explosives dominated the tactics of warfare.

An American rear-admiral in recent years has been quoted as saying that 'The man with the knife is the man who does the conquering. Nations can be softened up by bombs and rockets, but it requires a man with a knife to go in and actually take the country.' In the Second World War, the Bowie knife became a United States Army and Navy side-arm, while the British Commando knife embodied the same principles.

What is the origin of this comparatively modern yet world-famous fighting weapon, its points of difference from other knives—whether dirks, daggers or hunting knives?

The Bowie was usually larger and heavier than other types of knife, its blade measuring approximately 14 or 16 in. in the larger sizes. The blades of smaller Bowie knives might be as short as 8 or 9 in.

James Bowie, for whom the first knife of this kind was made—and who gave it its name—was born in 1799 in Logan, Kentucky, of Scottish emigrant stock. It appears that he left his home when about eighteen years old, and that for a living he relied mainly on cutting and selling lumber. His brother, John Bowie, described him at maturity as being 6 ft. tall and weighing 180 lb. Pioneering, then land speculation, made him a man of substance, but never diverted him from hunting and adventure.

In about 1826, Bowie became involved in the political strife of the day. This well suited his fiery, impulsive nature, but resulted in his being shot at and wounded by a sheriff during an altercation when he was un-armed. So enraged was Bowie at his helplessness during this incident that thereafter he always carried a sheathed hunting knife.

Later, as life became more strenuous and dangerous, he devised a

Fig. 63. Nineteenth-century Bowie daggers and hunting knives made in Sheffield

From left to right:
Bowie knife with 6-in. blade and 5-in. handle.
Bowie with 8-in. blade and 4¾-in. handle.
Dagger with 8½-in. blade and 5½-in. handle.
Dagger with 10-in. blade and 5-in. handle.
Hunting knife with 14-in. blade and 5-in. handle.
Sheaths are of leather and silver.

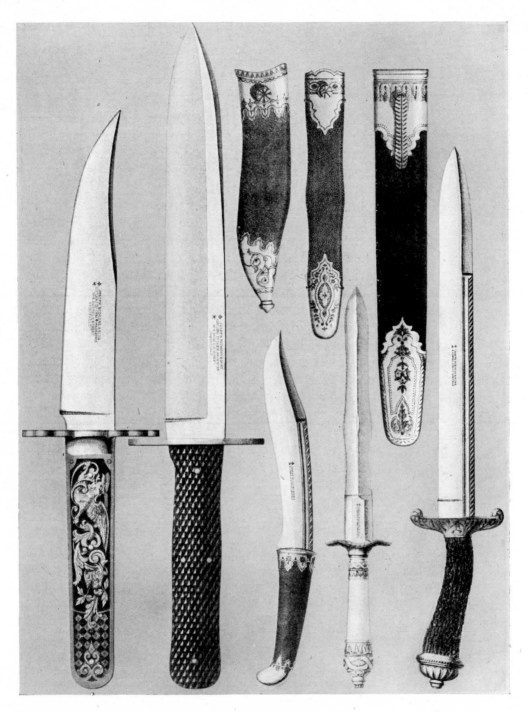

193

knife that was much heavier in character and which was suitable both for hunting and fighting. This was to become known throughout the world as the Bowie.

Widely differing accounts of Bowie's character have been recorded in history, particularly in his later years, when his adventures became legendary. Although his exploits have been described as those of a desperado, many of the reports were contradictory, including even those contained in works of reference which should be beyond dispute.

These conflicting accounts seem to have originated from the fact that gamblers, toughs, adventurers and mountebanks adopted the Bowie knife as their favourite weapon in a period when lawlessness was rife and the duel a common means of settling disputes. An attorney of the time is reputed to have said in court that the Bowie was the speediest and surest way of settling an argument. He was merely reflecting the feeling of the time.

There is much evidence, however, that Colonel James Bowie might well have been more of a gentleman than most of his contemporaries. In fact, when his brother bearded some of his detractors in the Press, charging them with giving sensational and false reports, apologies were soon forthcoming.

The final scene in a most colourful, energetic life shows Bowie raising a regiment in the Texan War of Independence, in which he fought and died courageously. His body was ignominiously disposed of on a pyre constructed by the victors, and an eyewitness stated that his famous knife was cast into the flames. Another account stated that the knife was later exhibited in the Alamo Museum—the fort that Bowie had given his life defending in 1836.

The Bowie met the demand for a knife heavy enough to take the place of a sword and which would decapitate an opponent, be sufficiently pointed for use as a dagger and which could be thrown.

A style of Bowie that was produced specially for throwing became known as the 'Arkansas toothpick'. Designed with the weight so distributed that it turned twice in a throwing range of 30 ft., it was usually carried in a holster at the back of the owner's neck. From this position it could be drawn rapidly in an emergency and thrown with deadly effect, used, no doubt, as an auxiliary weapon to the Bowie itself.

In the larger cities of the south-western states, schools were set up to teach the proper handling of Bowie knives. The extensive use of these weapons was later deemed such a menace to the safety of the public, in town as well as country, that laws were passed to suppress their possession, presentation or disposal. The maximum penalty for infringement of these laws was a fine of $500 or imprisonment for six months. For using the Bowie or similar knives, or even for drawing them from their holsters, the penalty imposed was confinement in gaol for a period of not less than three years. Legislation such as this was adopted in the states of Tennessee, Alabama and Mississippi in 1837 to 1839.

Many young men, however, considered they hardly had any claim to

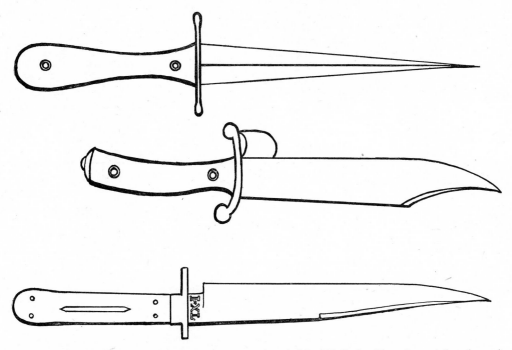

Fig. 64. Top to bottom: Arkansas 'tooth-pick'; U.S.A. Bowie with thumb guard; Sheffield made Bowie, bearing the Wostenholm mark, 'I-XL', one of a number of knives that Colonel James Bowie had made for him and distributed among his friends. It is said to be identical to a knife once shown in the Alamo Museum

manhood unless they carried a Bowie knife: the times were dangerous and incidents frequent.

When considering the development of the Bowie knife, it is necessary to bear in mind the part played by Sheffield, the cutlery centre of the world at that period. In the early part of the nineteenth century, these knives were for many years made by the craftsmen of Joseph Rodgers & Sons Ltd. from the best materials.

George Wostenholm & Son Ltd., of Washington Works, Sheffield, have abundant evidence of a close and early connection, not only with the American trade generally, through the personal visits made by the founder of the firm, George Wostenholm, as early as 1836—six years previously he had sent a representative to New York on business—but also with the Bowie knife.

There can be little doubt that Colonel James Bowie's first knife would have been made by a local blacksmith, but later he had twelve made by Wostenholm's. These had pearl handles and some of them were presented by Bowie to his friends.

After Bowie's abortive defence of Fort Alamo, San Antonio, Texas, in March, 1836, against the victorious assault of General Santa Anna, it can safely be assumed that it was one of these twelve knives that was found

---

Fig. 65. Knives from American Indian graves and United States and Canadian Museums

Left to right. Top row:

Not marked. From Ottawa Indian Graves, Michigan, now in Davenport Public Museum, Iowa.

Blade of $6\frac{1}{4}$-in. and haft of $4\frac{1}{8}$-in., not marked. From Ottawa Indian Grave, now in Davenport Public Museum.

Blade of $7\frac{1}{8}$-in., marked 'Jukes Coulson Stokes and Co., Sheffield'. From U.S. National Museum, Washington, D.C.

Blade of $8\frac{1}{4}$-in. and haft of $3\frac{5}{8}$-in., marked 'Jukes Coulson Stokes and Co., Sheffield'. From U.S. National Museum.

Blade of 6-in. and haft of $3\frac{1}{2}$-in., marked 'Van Wort and Naylor' (Sheffield merchants). From U.S. National Museum.

Blade of $5\frac{3}{4}$-in. and haft of $3\frac{7}{8}$-in., marked 'Beaver Falls Cutlery Company'—of America. From Museum of American Indians, N.Y.C.

Brass moon and stars inlaid in horn scales. Blade of $6\frac{3}{4}$-in. and haft of $3\frac{5}{8}$-in., marked 'Van Wort and Naylor'. From Museum of American Indians.

Blade of 6-in. and haft of $4\frac{1}{2}$-in., marked 'Atlas Works'. From Museum of American Indians.

Middle row:

Blade of $6\frac{1}{8}$-in., and haft of $4\frac{1}{8}$-in., marked 'Anglo-Pacific Cutlery Co., Sheffield'. From Missouri Historical Society Museum, St. Louis.

Fox mark on blade of first knife in bottom row.

Bottom row:

Sheffield knife blade adapted as Indian club, with device of fox. From Museum of American Indians.

Much worn blade, marked 'George Wostenholm, Sheffield'. From Ottawa Indian Grave, now in Davenport Public Museum.

Blade of 8-in. and haft of $4\frac{1}{2}$-in. Bowie type, marked 'Jno. Wilson, Sheffield'. From Royal Ontario Museum, Toronto.

Blade of $6\frac{1}{2}$-in. and reindeer haft. Not marked. From Royal Ontario Museum.

Not marked. From Royal Ontario Museum.

Clasp knife, not marked. From U.S. National Museum.

Photographs by Mr. and Mrs. Arthur Woodward, Los Angeles, California, by whose kind permission they are reproduced.

among the remains of his funeral pyre and which was on show until recent years at the Alamo Museum. (This knife has since disappeared from the Museum, presumably stolen.)

A descendant of James Bowie, Mr. J. Bryant of Milburn, New Jersey, possesses one of the original twelve knives. Illustrated in Fig. 64, it is marked with Wostenholm's trade mark 'I.XL' and name.

How early the term Bowie became generally used in the Sheffield trade cannot be decided by present evidence, but in 1837, Unwin and Rodgers were making and advertising 'American and Indian hunting and self-defence' knives, along with daggers and dirks.

In 1845, Wilson and Southern, also of Sheffield, were offering 'Buenos Aires daggers and hunting knifes . . . with sheaths to suit them'. These dates, however, do not give any idea of the vast quantity of Bowie knives that were exported from Sheffield during the late eighteenth and early nineteenth centuries to all parts of the world.

A large selection of Bowie and other knives that have been recovered from the graves of North American Indians is on show in museums throughout the United States and Canada. Among the marks on them are those of the Anglo-Pacific Cutlery Company, Sheffield; Jno. Wilson, Sheffield; Atlas Works; Van Work and Naylor, merchants, Sheffield; Beaver Falls Cutlery Company (U.S. made); Juke Coulson Stokes and Co., Sheffield; George Wostenholm, Sheffield; and a device of a fox on a Sheffield knife blade that had been adapted for use as an Indian club (Fig. 65).

The manufacturers and craftsmen of Sheffield did more than assist the development of the Bowie knife: they set the pattern for the American cutlery industry and influenced styles throughout the world. They made and sold the finest qualities of cutlery, establishing a reputation second to none, both in England and in countries overseas and to prove their versatility produced utility cutlery of good quality steel, but at a price to appeal to native users in under-developed areas.

The fine, artistic qualities of the nineteenth century cutlers of Sheffield are not likely to be equalled again. There is, in fact, very little demand to-day for delicately produced cutlery. Manufacturers are, however, making high quality wares of simple, fluid designs that symbolise the times in which they live—the era of the jet and the atom. That has been so throughout the history of cutlery-making, for the progress of man can be traced by the cutting tools he used—from the Stone Age to stainless steel.

CORONATION CUTLERY

CORONATION CUTLERY

THE Coronation of Elizabeth II in June, 1953, was marked by the production of thousands of cutlery souvenirs in varying degrees of quality.

A special Coronation sterling silver assay mark was produced in Sheffield and was first used on silver goods in November, 1952. The mark, reproduced on page 199, comprises the head of Queen Elizabeth II, the initials (J.R.H.) of the manufacturers, registered at the Sheffield Assay Office, the crown, signifying that the article was tested and marked at the Assay Office, the lion—the national symbol, and the letter K, the token letter used in Sheffield to denote the year 1952.

Table knives and forks, spoon sets, child's cutlery sets, desk knives, cake and bread knives, butter and cheese knives are a few of the items of cutlery produced in Sheffield as souvenirs. Illustrated in Fig. 67 are sterling silver spoons produced in anticipation of the Coronation of Edward, Duke of Windsor.

Although the Victoria and Albert Museum has in its collection, pieces of cutlery produced specially for kings and queens of former times, these were not made for general use and the production of cutlery for Coronation souvenirs is a modern innovation.

Fig. 66. Examples of Sheffield cutlery made to commemorate the Coronation of Elizabeth II

(*Top*): Two forks, electro-silver-plated on nickel silver (E.P.N.S.); three E.P.N.S. spoons.

(*Bottom, left*): These knives are made from Sheffield stainless steel with grained xylonite handles. The small fruit knife has coloured handle. The cake knife and bread knives have "Kleen Cut" edges, patented by Needham Veall and Tyzack Ltd., who made all the knives in the lower part of this illustration.

(*Bottom, right*): Stainless steel paper knife, and cake knife with stainless steel blade and xylon handle.

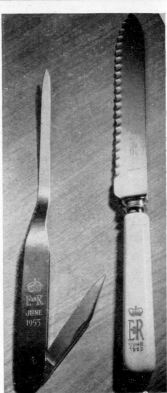

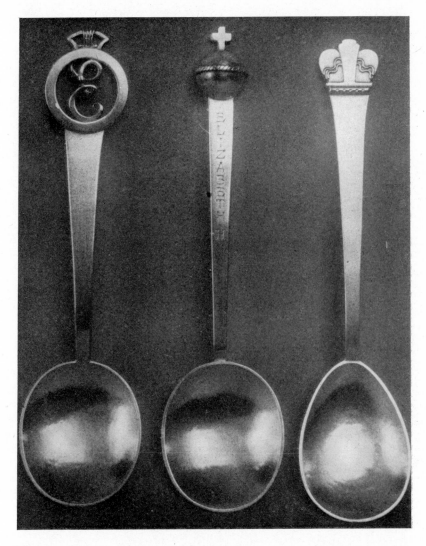

Fig. 67. Hand-made sterling silver spoons, made to mark
Coronation of Elizabeth II. (By Joyce R. Himsworth)

Fig. 68. Hand-made sterling silver spoons, made in anticipation of the Coronation of Edward, Duke of Windsor. Centre spoon is engraved, while those on either side are inlaid in black neillo. (By Joyce R. Himsworth. From the collection of Edwin Goddard Stokes)

INDEX

SET IN TWELVE POINT MONOTYPE PLANTIN AND PRINTED IN GREAT BRITAIN
BY THE CAMELOT PRESS LIMITED SOUTHAMPTON